THE MEDIEVAL LIBRARY UNDER
THE GENERAL EDITORSHIP OF
SIR ISRAEL GOLLANCZ, Litt.D., F.B.A.

TRANSLATIONS FROM THE
ICELANDIC

The Thor Cross, Kirk Bride, Isle of Man,
from 'Manx Crosses' by P. M. C. Kermode, F.S.A. Scot.

TRANSLATIONS FROM THE ICELANDIC: BEING SELECT PASSAGES INTRODUCTORY TO ICELANDIC LITERATURE TRANSLATED AND EDITED BY THE REV. W. C. GREEN, M.A.

COOPER SQUARE PUBLISHERS, INC.
NEW YORK
1966

Published 1966 by Cooper Square Publishers, Inc.
59 Fourth Avenue, New York, N. Y. 10003
Library of Congress Catalog Card No. 66-30733

Printed in the United States of America
by Noble Offset Printers, Inc., New York, N. Y. 10003

INTRODUCTION

WITHIN the last fifty years there has been a growing interest in old Icelandic literature. The excellent translation of the Njalssaga by the late Sir G. Dasent (1861), with the introductory matter, did much to awaken this. Other sagas have since been put within the reach of English readers. For some years now there has existed the Viking Club, a society for all interested in the north, issuing its annual Saga-books with valuable papers, and promising to publish still more. And the study of the Icelandic language has been now rendered easily possible: it was before beset with difficulties. We have a good Lexicon (Vigfússon's grounded on Cleasby) and several grammars. In old times an English student had only Haldorson's Lexicon, must approach nearly everything through Latin translations, could do little without knowledge of the Danish and Swedish tongues and of the learned authors who wrote in them.

It is true that readers of Gray knew "The Fatal
Sisters," and "The Descent of Odin," "Odes from
the Norse Tongue."   But after all, Gray's knowledge
of things Norse must have been mainly through Latin
translations.   Then too our great northern wizard
Scott had given us glimpses of manners and customs
Scandinavian in the "Pirate"; but all this was only
a slight lifting of the veil.   We all knew that most of
the days of our week were named from Scandinavian
deities, and this was about the sum of what most
persons knew.   Few Englishmen were aware that
there were histories of Norway's kings from about the
middle of the ninth century, carefully and in the main
trustworthily written, that there were biographies of
men of note, family histories through several genera-
tions, excellent pictures of the life and manners of a
people who spoke a language near akin to our own,
who were venturous sailors over rough seas, brave
warriors—freebooters certainly, but in an age when
war was astir everywhere, and raids on an enemy's
country brought no shame.   Nor were these bold
Northmen only fighters.   Besides their "long-ships"
for war, they had heavier ships of burden, merchant-
vessels, with which, "when spring came and ice was
loosed," they sailed from land to land.   Often did a

bold trader visit our English shores, and ship therefrom cargoes of meal and honey : " he came southward
(as a Saga words it) to London Bridge, and there set
up his ship on rollers." England indeed is much
spoken of in the Sagas, her kings are often mentioned,
from Alfred onwards. Norsemen, and especially Icelanders, fought in some important battles in our
country. We read much too about Scotland and the
" Southern isles," and Ireland.

Now mark that what information we have about
these times and places we owe chiefly to Icelandic
authors : it was they who carefully kept these records,
handed down by memory from eyewitnesses, and then
written, so soon as writing became an art generally
practised ; which would be when Christianity became
the accepted faith in Iceland, A.D. 1000. In fact the
best literature that we possess about the north for
some four hundred years (860-1260) is in Icelandic.

But how came it to pass that this *ultima Thule*, this
island of frost and snow, gave us these treasures? To
answer this something must be said of the early settlement of Iceland.

Some Irish monks visited Iceland about A.D. 825,
but they did not permanently stay there : it was seen
by voyagers soon afterwards, and named Snowland

and Iceland.   But the first settler who remained to
dwell there was Ingolf: he came from Norway in 874.
Then from Norway soon followed others; the deter-
mining cause being their wish to escape from the
overbearing (as they deemed it) of Harold Fairhair,
who, having become sole king in Norway, was chang-
ing the old laws of land tenure.   These changes drove
abroad many high-spirited independent chiefs and
freemen.   Lands were to be had for the taking in
empty Iceland.   So thither they went: and this im-
migration continued for about sixty years, some settlers
also flowing in from Ireland during the same period.
It is called *Landnamatid*, "landtaking time."

These immigrants peopled pretty thickly all the
shores of the island, indented by firths on the west
and north, with dales that penetrated far inland.
They were, we must remember, of the best blood in
Norway, many of the foremost for bravery and intelli-
gence; this peopling of Iceland was no sending out
of the refuse or baser sort.   They remained independent of king or government outside the island,
they established laws and courts for themselves.

After their departure there came to be formed on
the mainland of Scandinavia new dialects of the
language, Norwegian, Swedish, Danish: but the Ice-

landers kept their old tongue unchanged, indeed it is little changed even at the present day. It may be that this permanence of the language helped them to preserve its treasures better than could those whom they left behind. Their independence too, and freedom in some measure from the quarrels and contests of the mainland kingdoms, may have left the minds and hands of their able and learned men more free for literary work. At all events they did prove able treasurers of old myths, legends, and traditions. A literature sprang up on this island superior to anything contemporaneous on the mainland. A full classified list of Icelandic works and authors may be found at the beginning of Vigfússon's Lexicon. Here a very brief account of a few of these may suffice.

The older Edda, called also Sæmund's Edda, contains the earliest compositions in Icelandic that we have. These are poems: they were collected by Sæmund the learned, who died A.D. 1133: but no doubt they were composed long before. They are mythical lays or songs about gods and heroes.

There is another Edda called the younger or prose Edda. This was put together by Snorri Sturluson (who lived 1176-1241). In its first part are given in prose the chief myths about the gods: in the second there is much of verse both from the older Eddic lays and from other poets. A large part of it is called *Skaldskapar-mál*, 'Poetic diction.' One might term it a sort of *Gradus* or *Ars Poetica*. Many old legends are given in it by way of explaining metaphor or 'Kennings' used by poets.

The earliest Icelandic verse is alliterative, not rhyming. It is simple in construction, the sentences are very short. Yet it is in parts hard to understand, because it contains old words of uncertain meaning, and obscure allusions, and curious periphrases, or 'kennings' as they are termed. The 'kennings' of the older poets were really poetical metaphors : but later bards came to love fanciful and roundabout expressions, purposely to puzzle the hearer, and with these the impromptu staves and eulogies of the court-poetry are over-loaded. Those curious about kennings may consult the early part of the *Corpus Poeticum Boreale*, or pp. xi., xii. of my Introduction to the Egils-saga.

Two translations from Eddic poems will be found in this collection ; three of Egil's longer poems, and detached staves in several of the prose extracts.

But the Icelandic prose is (*me judice*) more interesting and more valuable than the Icelandic verse. No

doubt we must go to the verse to find the theogony, the
religious legends of the far north : and to compare
these with the religious writings of other lands will
always be an attractive study.   But I do not think
that we can say that the Scandinavian theology much
ruled or affected the life and practice of the people in
the times of which we read.   Their religious services
do not come very prominently before us in the histories of kings or citizens.   Sacrifices and feasts are
mentioned now and again ; their most esteemed warriors fight and feast as did Odin and Thor, and hope
after death to be welcomed 'at the table of the Ases.
But the faith in these old powers had, even a century
before the acceptance of Christianity, become rather
faint and lifeless.   Of this a fair example may be seen
in Arnljot Gellini, who—a supposed heathen when he
comes before king Olaf—being asked about his faith,
answers that he believes in his own might and main,
that hitherto this faith has sufficed him.   And again,
even earlier, Egil, mourning for his son Bodvar, says
that he will henceforth renounce Odin, who has proved
false in his need.   Plainly in the tenth century
the Norsemen's faith in their theology sat loose
upon them, and Christianity thus found easier acceptance.

Probably in the literature of every land verse came before prose, because more easily remembered. But the Sagas too were doubtless learnt by heart and told long before they were written. And the telling was kept truthful by public opinion : no falsehood or unfairness was tolerated. Of this we have proofs : for example, Gunnar Lambi's son, who told the story of the Burning unfairly at earl Sigurd's board, was held to be deservedly therefore punished (Njalssaga ch. 154). Some story-tellers no doubt were better than others : but listeners would not tolerate unfairness, or much variation in facts. Something like this we find nowadays : children, when hearing a well-known story, are impatient of change, and insist upon correcting the teller back to the old version. And so the Sagas were kept faithfully, and told by some of the best story-tellers ever known, till in more clerkly times they came to be written down. The events recorded often go back at least as far as the first settlement of Iceland.

In very few cases do we know the name of the saga-writers. Those of the Norwegian kings were gathered together in one book under the name of *Heimskringla*, "World's-circle," by Snorri Sturluson ; but there are other recensions or editions of some of these lives : and the same is the case with other sagas.

There is a pretty general agreement that of the
family histories Njalssaga for interest and style stands
first. Gudbrand Vigfússon, quoted in Burnt Njal
p. vi., has said that it is to all others " as gold to
brass" : this is surely too much to say. There are
many sagas really good : I should put Egilssaga a good
second. But enough has now been said to vindicate
the value of this old Icelandic literature.

The collection of translations now offered will be
found fairly representative. They were made at
different times, mostly within the last twenty-four
years, though my earliest Icelandic studies began
twenty years earlier, when helps were few. Some
few passages may now be found in other English
versions. Two of the ballads from the Njala appeared
in *Blackwood's Magazine* in 1890. Messrs. Blackwood
have kindly given me permission to include them
here.

When one renders good Icelandic prose into English, there is not much temptation to stray far from
the original. But the verse translations in this volume
are also really translations, not loose imitations ; they
are closer (I think) than most verse translations that
I know. Alliterative has been rendered by alliterative, rhyming by rhyming.

The ballads were an experiment first made in the two from the Njala in 1890; this saga had already been well Englished by Dasent. Parts of the saga were selected that seemed to lend themselves to ballad treatment. Afterwards I tried the same method with two more scenes from Njala, and two from the story of Gunnlaug Snake-tongue (already translated by Magnússon). In these verse translations from prose some liberty of rearrangment has been assumed; but the facts in my verse are just those told in the prose; nothing has been added that the prose did not fairly suggest.

Is a defence needed for Hallgrim Pétursson, the last poet in my translations? He was, compared with my other originals, a modern Icelander, but he was a very remarkable writer. Vigfússon has termed some of his poems "the flower of Icelandic poetry, old as well as modern." Be this my apology for including some specimens from him in this collection.

W. C. GREEN.

CONTENTS

PROSE TRANSLATIONS

THOR AND HRUNGNIR

This story is told by Bragi, the god of poetry, to Ægir, a magician, who visited the gods at Asgard.

THOR had fared eastwards to fight trolls; but Odin rode Sleipnir to Jötunheim, and came to the giant named Hrungnir. Then asked Hrungnir who ever was he with golden helm that rode wind and wave. "He hath," said he, "a wondrous good horse." Odin said he would there wager his head that no horse so good could be found in Jötunheim. 'Twas a good horse indeed, said Hrungnir, yet declared that he had a horse of far longer stride; it was named Goldmane. And Hrungnir was wroth, and he leapt upon his horse, and galloped after Odin, thinking to pay him out for his boastful words. Odin galloped so fast that he was ever in advance on the opposite hill, and Hrungnir was in such giant fury that before he was aware he had gotten past the fence-gate of the Ases. But when he came to the hall door the Ases asked him in to drink. Then were brought those cups out of which Thor was wont to drink, and Hrungnir tossed them off one and all. And when he was well drunk, then was there no stint of big words: he would (he declared) take up Valhalla and carry it to Jötunheim, but Asgard he would sink, and slay all the gods save Freyja and Sif, whom he would bear home with him. And now Freyja came to fill his cups, and he declared he would drink up all the Ases' ale.

But when the Ases were weary of his monster strength, then called they Thor, who presently came into the hall, bearing aloft the hammer, and he was right wroth. "Who," he asked, "ruled this, that hound-witted giants should drink here? Who gave Hrungnir leave to be here with peace in Valhalla? Why should Freyja fill the cup for him, as at the banquet of the Ases?" Then answered Hrungnir, looking at Thor with no friendly eyes, that Odin bade him in to drink, and that he had his warrant of peace. Then said Thor that Hrungnir would rue this bidding ere he won out. It were but little honour to Asa-Thor, said Hrungnir, to slay him weaponless; 'twere more proof of courage if he dared fight with him on the border land at Griotuna-gard.

"And 'twas great fool's work," said he, "that I left my shield and hone behind: if I had here my weapons, we twain would even now try the combat: but I shall count it in thee a dastard's act if thou slay me weaponless."

Thor was not one to shun single combat on this challenge to the duel, which none had ever offered him before.

So then Hrungnir went his way, and galloped hard till he came to Jötunheim. And his journey was much talked of among the giants; as was also this, that a meeting was appointed of himself and Thor. Much was at stake (thought the giants) on this, whether of the twain would win the victory. They might look for evil from Thor, should Hrungnir fall, for he was their strongest.

Then did the giants make at Griotuna-gard a man of clay: nine miles high he was, and three miles broad between the armpits. But they could get no heart big enough to match him, till they took one out of a mare, and that was not steady when Thor came. Hrungnir had the heart which is so famous, of hard-stone, and spiked, three-cornered, like the Runic character afterwards made, which is called Hrungnir's heart. His head was also of stone; his shield too

was a stone broad and thick, and he held this shield
before him, as he stood at Griotuna-gard awaiting
Thor; but he had for weapon a hone, and this he
brandished over his shoulder, and he seemed no easy
foe.   On one side of him stood the clay man,
Mökkur-calf, but he was sore afraid, running with
water for very fear, 'tis said, when he saw Thor.   To
the appointed lists came Thor, and with him Thialfi.
Then ran Thialfi forward to where Hrungnir stood,
and said to him: "Thou standest unwarily, O giant;
thou holdest thy shield before thee.   But Thor hath
seen thee, and he travels by the nether way, below
the earth, and will come at thee from beneath."
Then Hrungnir cast his shield under his feet, and
stood thereon, but wielded with two hands his hone.
Soon he saw fiery flashes and heard mighty thunder-
ings; then he saw Thor in Asa fury, who came on
fiercely, and brandishing his hammer cast it from afar
at Hrungnir.   Hrungnir, uplifting the hone with
both hands, cast it against him: and hone met
hammer in flight, whereupon the hone brake in
sunder, one part falling to earth, (whence are
quarried all hones) but the other part dashed into
Thor's head, so that he fell forward on the ground.
But the hammer Mjöllnir came full on Hrungnir's

forehead, and shattered his skull to pieces. And prone he fell upon Thor, so that his foot lay over Thor's neck. But Thialfi fought with Mökkur-calf and slew him with little glory.

Then went Thialfi to Thor, and would fain lift Hrungnir's foot from off him, but had not the strength. And all the Ases came thither when they heard that Thor was fallen, and would lift the foot off him, but they availed nothing. At last came Magni, son of Thor and Iron-Chopper, he was then three years old; he thrust Hrungnir's foot off Thor, and said: "See, father, what shame is it that I come so late: I ween I would have smitten this giant to death with my fist had I encountered him." Thor then stood up, and greeted his son well, and said he would become a stout fellow. "And I will give thee," he said, "the horse Goldmane, which was Hrungnir's." Whereat Odin spake, and said that Thor did wrong in giving that good horse to an ogress' son and not to his own father. Thor went home to Thrudvang with the hone still standing in his head. Then came thither the Sibyl named Groa, wife of Orvandil the valiant; she chaunted her charms over Thor till the hone began to loosen. And when Thor found that, and thought there was hope of the hone coming out, he wished to reward

Groa for her leech-craft and to make her glad. So he told her these tidings, how he had waded from the North over ice-waves, and had carried on his back in a basket Orvandil from the North out of Jötunheim : adding this, that one toe of his had stood out of the basket and got frozen, wherefore he, Thor, broke it off and cast it up to heaven, and made a star of it there, which was named " Orvandil's toe." Thor said withal that it would not be long ere Orvandil came home. Whereat Groa was so glad that she remembered no more her charms, and the hone became no looser. And it stands yet in Thor's head.

Wherefore men are warned not to cast a hone across the floor : for then the hone moves in Thor's head.

WHY IS GOLD CALLED SIF'S HAIR?

In the part of the Edda called *Skaldskaparmál*, "poetic diction," several "kennings" or poetic periphrases, are explained by stories. Whether the kenning came from the story, or the story from the kenning, may in some cases be doubtful. There are learned critics who think nearly all legendary stories founded on words or metaphors. Sif is mother earth with her golden grain : several of the kennings for gold are explicable apart from their stories.

LOKI LAUFEY'S son, to show his craft, had clipped off all the hair of Sif Thor's wife. But when Thor knew of it, he took Loki, and threatened to break every bone of him, till he swore this, that he would get the Swart elves to make for Sif a golden head of hair that should grow just like other hair. So Loki went to those dwarves, who are called Ivald's sons, and they made the hair, and made withal the ship Skidbladnir, and the spear belonging to Odin, which is named Gungnir.

Then Loki wagered his head with the dwarf named Brokk, that his brother Sindri would not make three precious things as good as these.

To the smithy they went, and then Sindri laid a swine-skin on the hearth of the forge, and bade Brokk blow and stay not in his blowing till he should take from the hearth what he had put in. But no sooner had he gone out from the smithy, while the other blew, than a fly settled on the blower's hand and bit; yet he blew on as before, till the smith took his work from the hearth, and lo, it was a boar with bristles of gold. Next he laid on the hearth gold, and bade the other blow and leave not blowing before he came back; he then went out. But the fly came now and settled upon his neck and bit twice as sharply: yet he stayed not his blowing till the smith took from the hearth the gold ring that is named Draupnir. Then he laid iron on the hearth, and bade his brother blow, and said it would be no good work if the blast failed. And now the fly settled between his eyes and bit the eyelids: but when blood fell into his eyes, so that he could not see, then as quickly as possible he made a snatch with his hands and wiped off the fly, while the bellows were sinking. And just then came in the smith, and said that this would go near to spoil the whole work that was on the hearth: and he then took out from the hearth a hammer.

All these precious things he gave into the hands of his brother Brokk, and bade him bear them to Asgard and decide the wager.

Now when Brokk and Loki brought out these precious works, then the Ases took their seats on the doom-stools; and that judgment was to stand which should be pronounced by Odin, Thor, and Frey. Then gave Loki to Odin the spear Gungnir, to Thor the hair which Sif was to have, to Frey Skidbladnir: and he explained the virtues of these marvellous works: how the spear never stayed in the place it had stricken; how the hair would grow to the flesh so soon as it came to Sif's head; how Skidbladnir would get a fair wind so soon as ever the sail was hoisted aloft, and how the ship could be folded up like cloth and kept in a bag if the owner wished.

And then Brokk brought out his precious works: he gave the ring to Odin, and said that every ninth night would drip from it eight rings of the same weight as itself: but to Frey he gave the boar, and said that it could run through air and water by night and by day more swiftly than any horse; and never was it so dark by night or in the world of darkness, that there was not enough light where the boar went, such radiance beamed from his bristles. Then gave he to Thor the hammer, and said that he might smite as hard as he would whatever was in his way, and never would the hammer fail; and, should he cast it at anything, it would never miss the mark, nor ever fly so far that it would not come back to hand: and, if he wished it, the hammer would become so small that he might keep it within his shirt-bosom: but one fault it had, the handle was somewhat short.

The judgment of the Ases was that of all the precious works the hammer was the best, and therein lay the chiefest safeguard against the Frost-giants: and so the dwarf was judged to have won the wager.

Whereupon Loki offered to ransom his head. That, answered the dwarf, was past hoping. "Take me, then," said Loki. But when he would have taken him, lo! he was ever so far away. For Loki indeed had shoes wherewith he could travel air and water. Then the dwarf asked Thor to take him: he did so: and then the dwarf would fain have chopped off Loki's head. Loki said, "You have a right to the head, but not to the neck." Then the dwarf took a thong and knife to bore a hole in Loki's lips and stitch together his mouth, but the knife would

not pierce through. Then said he that better for
this end were his brother's awl; and at once as he
named it the awl was there: and it pierced the lips.
So he stitched the lips together, and drew the ends
of the thong out at the two lip-corners.

OTTER'S FINE

THE explanation of this kenning for gold leads to the story of the Volsungs and Niflungs; how the gold proved a curse to its possessors. *Auri sacra fames* brings wickedness and ruin. Morris has expanded this legend into a beautiful poem.

THE story goes that three of the Ases, Odin, Loki, and Honir, were travelling to explore the world. They came to a river, and this river they followed up to a waterfall, and by the waterfall was an otter, who had caught a salmon out of the pool, and was eating it, dozing the while. Then Loki took up a stone and cast it at the otter, and hit him on the head; and he was proud of his prize, having by one blow caught both otter and salmon. They took then the salmon and the otter, and carried them along; and soon they came to a house and went in. The goodman of the house was named Hreidmar; he was a powerful man and of great magic cunning. The Ases asked a night's lodging there, saying that

they had with them food enough, and they showed
the goodman their venison. But when Hreidmar
saw the otter he called his sons Fafnir and Regin,
and told them that Otter their brother was slain,
telling them also who had done this. Then father
and sons set upon the Ases and bound them, declaring
this of the otter, that he was Hreidmar's son. The
Ases offered to redeem their lives with as much
money as Hreidmar himself should determine; and
atonement on these terms was agreed and sworn to.

Then the otter was flayed, and Hreidmar took his
skin, and said to them that they must fill the skin
with red gold, and with gold cover it all outside, and
these should be the terms of atonement.

Odin then sent Loki to the Swart Elves' world:
and he came to the dwarf who is named Andvari.
He was a fish in the water; but Loki caught him,
and required of him as the ransom of his life all the
gold that he had in his stone chamber. And when
they came into the stone chamber, the dwarf carried
thereout all the gold that he had, and it was a very
great hoard. Then the dwarf slipped under his hand
one little gold ring; but Loki saw this, and bade him
let go the ring. The dwarf begged he would not
take from him the ring, saying that he could increase

his wealth from the ring if he kept it.   Loki said he
should not keep back even one penny; and he took
from him the ring, and went out.   But the dwarf
declared that this ring should prove a bane to the
head of every one who should own it.   Loki said
that he liked that well: and, "This will I do," said he,
"that thy words may hold good, I will repeat them in
the ears of him who takes this ring."

He then went back to Hreidmar and showed Odin
the gold.   But when Odin saw the ring, it seemed to
him a beautiful one, and he took it from among the
money, paying over the gold to Hreidmar.   Hreidmar
then filled the otter's skin as full as he could, and when
full, he set it up.   Then came Odin, who was to cover
all the skin with gold.   Which done, he called Hreidmar to see whether all the skin was covered.   Hreidmar
looked thereat, and considered carefully, and he saw
one hair of the beard: this he bade him cover; else
was their atonement void.   Whereupon Odin drew
ont the ring, and therewith covered the hair of the
beard, saying that they were now quit of the otter's-
fine.   And when Odin had taken back his spear, and
Loki his shoes, and they had nothing more to fear,
then said Loki that what Andvari had said should
hold good; this ring and this gold should be the bane

of whoso owned them. And this held good in after time.

And now is the story told why gold is called Otter's-fine, or the Ases' need-fine, or metal of strife.

What more is there to tell of this gold?

Hreidmar took the gold as atonement for his son: but Fafnir and Regin demanded some of it as atonement for their brother. And when Hreidmar would not give them a single penny, then the brothers wrought this wickedness, that they slew their father for the sake of the gold. Then Regin demanded that Fafnir should halve the gold with him. Whereto Fafnir answered that it was little likely he would share the gold with his brother, when for the sake of the gold he had slain his father. And he bade Regin get him gone; else would he fare as Hreidmar had fared. Fafnir had now taken the helmet that had been Hreidmar's, and set it on his own head; it was called the Helm of Terror, and struck fear into all living beholders. He had taken withal the sword called Hrotti. Regin had the sword called Refill. He therefore fled away, but Fafnir went up on Gnita-heath, where he made him a lair, and took upon him the form of a serpent, and lay on the gold. But Regin went to Hjalnek, king in Thioda, and became

there his smith : he then took as foster-son Sigurd,
son of Sigmund, which was the son of Volsung and
Hjordisa Eylim's daughter.   Sigurd was of all war-
kings most renowned for birth, and strength, and
courage.   Regin told him where Fafnir lay on the
gold, and egged him on to seek it.   And Regin forged
for him a sword, Gram it was named ; which was so
sharp that, when Sigurd held it in running water, it
cut through a flock of wool that drifted with the
stream upon its edge.   With this sword, moreover,
Sigurd clove Regin's anvil right down to the block.

After that Sigurd and Regin went together up to
Gnita-heath : there Sigurd digged a pit in the way
that Fafnir took, and therein he lay hidden.   But·
when Fafnir creeping to the water came over the pit,
Sigurd thrust the sword up under him, and that was
his bane.   Then came Regin and said that Sigurd
had slain his brother, and he offered these terms of
atonement, that Sigurd should take Fafnir's heart and
roast it with fire : but he, Regin, lay down and drank
of the blood of Fafnir, and then laid him down to
sleep.

Now as Sigurd was roasting the heart, when he
thought it would be quite roasted, he felt it with his
finger to try how hard it was : but the froth ran out

from the heart on his finger, and scalded him, so he put his finger to his mouth. No sooner had the heart's blood touched his tongue than he knew the speech of birds, and understood what the woodpeckers were saying, which sat in the boughs.   Said one:

> "There sits Sigurd
> Juice-besprinkled,
> The heart of Fafnir
> He roasts in fire.
> Wise, as we ween,
> Were this gold-spoiler,
> If the light-flashing
> Life-clot he ate."

Another sang:

> "There lies Regin,
> His plot he layeth,
> Betraying the youth
> Who trusts him well.
> In wrath he putteth
> Wrong words together,
> Bale he forgeth
> A brother to venge."

Wherefore Sigurd went nigh to Regin and slew him; then gat him to his horse, by name Gray, and rode till he came to Fafnir's lair: whence he took up the gold, bound it in bundles and laid it on Gray's back; he then mounted and rode on his way.

Now has the story been told which shows why gold is called Fafnir's lair or dwelling, and Gnita-heath's metal, and Gray's burden.

Now Sigurd rode on till he found a house on the fell; wherein was sleeping a woman: she wore a helmet and a coat of mail. He drew his sword and slit the coat of mail from off her: she then waked, and gave her name, Hildr. She is also called Brynhildr, and was a Valkyria. Thence Sigurd rode till he came to the king, named Gjuki, whose wife was named Grimhildr; their children were these, Gunnar, Högni, Gudrun, Gudny; and Gotthorm was Gjuki's stepson. There Sigurd dwelt long time: while there he took to wife Gudrun, Gjuki's daughter; and Gunnar and Högni sware brotherhood with Sigurd. Anon Sigurd and Gjuki's sons took their way to Atli, Budi's son, to ask Brynhildr, Atli's sister, to wife for Gunnar. She sate on Hindfell, and round her hall was a wavering fire; and she had vowed a vow to have that man only for husband who should dare to ride the wavering fire.

So they rode, Sigurd to wit, and the Gjukings (who are also called Niflungs) up on to the fell: and Gunnar was then to ride the wavering fire. He had the horse named Goti, but that horse dared not leap into the

flame. Then Sigurd and Gunnar exchanged semblances and names; for the horse Gray would go
under no man but Sigurd. And Sigurd leapt on
Gray, and rode the wavering flame. On that eve he
made his bridal with Brynhildr; but when they came
to bed he drew his sword Gram from the sheath, and
laid it between them. But in the morning, when he
rose and clothed himself, he gave to Brynhildr as linen-
fee the gold ring which Loki had taken from Andvari,
while he took another ring from her as a memorial.
Then leapt Sigurd on his horse, and rode back to his
fellows; and he and Gunnar changed semblances
again, and they went back to Gjuki with Brynhildr.

Sigurd and Gudrun had two children, Sigmund
and Svanhildr.

Now it chanced one day that Brynhildr and Gudrun
went to the water to wash their hair. And when the
twain came to the river, Brynhildr waded out from
the shore into the stream, saying that she would not
bear on her head the water that ran out of Gudrun's
hair, seeing that she had a husband of better courage.
Then went Gudrun into the river after her, and said
that she herself ought for this cause to wash her hair
higher up in the river, since she had for husband one
whom neither Gunnar nor any one else in the world

could match for bravery, seeing that he slew Fafnir and Regin, and took heritage from them both. But Brynhildr answered, "This is worth more, that Gunnar rode the wavering fire, when Sigurd durst not do so." Laughed then Gudrun, and said, "Thinkest thou that Gunnar rode the wavering fire? He, I ween, was bedded beside thee who gave me this gold ring I wear: and that gold ring which thou hast on thy hand, and tookest as bridal-fee, is called Andvari's gift. Not Gunnar, as I think, sought that on Gnita-heath." Whereupon Brynhildr held her peace, and went home.

After this she egged on Gunnar and Högni to slay Sigurd. But since they were oath-sworn to Sigurd they egged on their brother Gotthorm to this slaying. He thrust Sigurd through with a sword while sleeping. But even as he got the wound Sigurd cast the sword Gram after the man, so that it clove him asunder in the midst. There fell Sigurd and his three-year-old son Sigmund whom they slew. Then Brynhildr pierced herself with a sword, and she was buried with Sigurd. But Gunnar and Högni took Fafnir's heritage and Andvari's gift, and ruled the land.

King Atli, Budli's son, Brynhildr's brother, then married Gudrun, whom Sigurd had had to wife: and they twain had children. And king Atli bade to his house Gunnar and Högni, and they accepted his bidding. But before they left home they hid Fafnir's heritage in the Rhine, nor has that gold ever since been found. Now king Atli had beforehand gathered great force, and he fought with Gunnar and Högni, and they were taken prisoners. Atli caused the heart to be cut out of Högni while yet alive, and that was his bane. Gunnar he had cast into a snake-pit. But a harp had privily been given to Gunnar, and upon this, his hands being bound, he so played with his toes that all the snakes were lulled to sleep, save one adder which darted at him, and piercing the cartilage of his breast-bone, thrust its head into the hollow, and hung there to his liver till he died.

Gunnar and Högni are called Niflungs as well as Gjukings: wherefore gold is called the Niflungs' treasure or heritage.

Soon afterwards Gudrun slew her two sons, and out of their skulls overlaid with gold and silver caused table-cups to be made. Then was held the funeral feast of the Niflungs. And at this feast Gudrun bade them serve to king Atli in these table-cups mead mixed with the blood of the boys, whose hearts she had roasted and served for the king to eat. Which

done, she told the king how it was, with many
horrible words. Of heady mead there was no stint,
so that most of the company slept where they sate.
In that same night went Gudrun to the king where
he sate, Högni's son being with her, and they attacked
him, and that was his bane. Then set they fire to
the hall and burned all that were therein. After
that she went to the sea and leapt in, wishing to
drown herself; but she drifted over the fjord and
came to the land ruled by Jonakr. He saw her, took
her to him, and married her. And they had three
sons, named thus, Sorli, Hamdir, and Erpr, who all
had hair raven-black like Gunnar, Högni and the
other Niflungs.

In that same land was being fostered Svanhildr,
daughter of Sigurd, fairest was she of women. King
Jormunrek the Great heard of this, and he sent his
son to ask her in marriage for him. But when he
came to Jonaker, then Svanhildr was delivered into
his hands, and he was to bring her to Jormunrek.
Then said Bikki, that it were more meet that Randver
should wed Svanhildr, both he and she being young,
whereas Jormunrek was old. This counsel was liked
well by the young men. But no sooner had Bikki
told this to the king than Jormunrek had his son

seized and led to the gallows. Then took Randver his hawk, and plucked off its feathers, and bade send it to his father: then he was hanged. But when Jormunrek saw the hawk, then came it to his mind that, as the hawk was unable to fly featherless, so was his kingdom weak, now that he was old and sonless. It so chanced that when King Jormunrek was riding back from the hunt in a wood with his train, Queen Svanhildr sate dressing her hair: then rode they at her and trode her under the horses' feet, and that was her bane.

This when Gudrun heard, she egged on her sons to avenge Svanhildr. And as they made them ready for the journey, she gave them breastplates and helmets so strong that no iron weapon could bite them; and she laid before them the counsel that on coming to King Jormunrek they should set upon him at night in his sleep; and Sorli and Hamdir should hew off his hands and feet, but Erpr his head. As they were in the way, they asked of Erpr what help they would have of him, if they met king Jormunrek. Such help, he answered, he would give them as hand gives foot. But so angry were they with their mother, who had sent them out with deadly words, that they resolved to do what she would think worst, and they killed Erpr because she loved him best.

Soon after, as Sorli was walking, he slipped with
one foot, but stayed himself with his hand. Then
said he, "Now hand helps foot: 'twere better that
Erpr lived."   And when they came upon king Jormunrek by night as he slept, and hewed off his hands
and his feet, he waked, and calling to his men bade
them wake.   And now said Hamdir, "His head
would be off, were Erpr alive." The men of the
king's guard stood up, and set upon them; yet with
weapons they could work them no hurt.   Then cried
Jormunrek that they should cast stones at them; and
they did so.   There fell Sorli and Hamdir: and thus
all the kin and seed of Gjuki found their death.

FRODI'S MILL

GRAIN is the gold of the earth, the truest and surest wealth : to this the legend may point. Also over-greed of treasure works ruin : *qui festinat ad divitias non erit insons.* The grinding maidens at the mill appear also in the poem of the mill, translated later on.

WHY is gold called Frodi's meal? To this belongs the following story. There was a son of Odin named Shield. He had his royal seat and rule in what is now called Denmark, but was then called Gotland. Shield had a son Fridleif, who ruled the land after him. Fridleif's son was named Frodi ; he took the kingdom after his father : it was in the time when Augustus Cæsar established peace over all the world ; then was Christ born. But as Frodi was the most powerful king in the north, the peace was called after him among all peoples of Danish tongue, being termed by northmen Frodi's peace. No man harmed another, even though he met before him his father's bane, or brother's, loose or bound. None then was a thief or robber, so that a gold ring lay long on Jalangs-heath untouched.

Now King Frodi was bidden to a feast in Sweden with a king named Tjölnir. There he bought two bondwomen named Fenja and Menja; they were tall and strong. At that time there were found in Denmark two millstones so large that no one was strong enough to turn them. And the mill had this nature, that it ground out whatever the grinder named before beginning to grind. This mill was called Grotti; and Hang-jaw was he named who gave King Frodi the mill.

King Frodi had the bondwomen led to the mill, and bade them grind gold, and peace, and bliss for Frodi. And he granted them no longer rest or sleep than while the cock was silent, or a stave could be sung. Then they sang, it is said, the song called Grotti's song. But ere they ceased they ground an army against Frodi; so that in the self-same night came the sea-king Mysing, and slew Frodi, and took there much booty. And so ended Frodi's peace.

HEDIN'S HOST

BATTLE is called 'tempest or snowstorm of Hedin's host,' and
weapons 'fires or wands of Hedin's host,' whereto belongs this
story.

THERE was a king named Högni, who had a
daughter by name Hildr. Now a king named
Hedin, son of Hjarrand, carried her away as a captive
of war, while Högni had gone to a council of kings.
But when Högni learnt that his realm had been
harried and his daughter borne away, he went with
his fleet to seek Hedin; and he heard of him that he
had sailed along the coast northwards. And when
king Högni came to Norway, he heard that Hedin
had sailed westwards over the sea. So Högni sailed
after him even to the Orkneys; and when he came
to the island called High Isle, there before him was
Hedin and his host. Hildr then went out to meet
her father, and offered him from Hedin a necklace as
an atonement, or, said she, Hedin was ready for

fight, and Högni had no mercy to expect from him. Högni answered his daughter harshly; and she on her return to Hedin said that Högni would accept no atonement, and bade him make ready for battle. They did so on either side: they went up on the island, and set their forces in array.

Then Hedin called to Högni his wife's father, offering atonement and much gold as compensation. But Högni made answer: "Too late thou offerest to atone, for I have now drawn Dains-leif, the sword forged by the dwarves, which must be a man's bane each time that it is bared, nor doth it ever fail of its stroke, nor can any wound therefrom be healed, though it be but a scratch." Then answered Hedin: "To vaunt a sword is not victory: I call that good which proves true to its lord."

Thereafter they had that battle which is called the fight of Hedin's host: and all that day they strove, but at eventide the kings went to their ships. But in the night Hildr went to the field, and by magic art she waked up all the dead: and the next day the kings again joined battle and fought, as likewise did all who had fallen on the day before. And that battle went on day after day thus: all men that fell, and all weapons that lay on the battle-field, shields and other gear, were turned into stone; but with the dawn all the dead men stood up and fought, and all the weapons were renewed.

And in songs it is said that Hedin's host will do this evermore, even unto the day of doom.

THE BATTLE OF VINHEATH

IT is thought by most that here is described the battle of
Brunanburh, fought A.D. 937, on which the Saxon chronicle
gives us a poem; though, according to the accepted chronology
of the Egil's Saga, the battle of Vinheath was some twelve years
earlier. Vinheath is placed by the Saga in Northumberland; so
is Brunanburh by most writers. Some, however, identify it
with Bromborough, in Cheshire. In the *Antiquary* of October,
1907, Mr. Francis W. T. Tudsbery is quoted as placing the
site of the battle in Wirral, part of Cheshire, but not exactly at Bromborough. He says about this site that "the
early accounts confirm each other, and are corroborated by the
natural features of the district." And "exactly correct is
the minute description of the battle-ground in Egil's Saga."
Many years ago, when translating this Saga, I thought that we
had here a description, truthful in the main, of a real battle.
Mr. Tudsbery's researches confirm this opinion. But some
maintain that Brunanburh was just south of the Humber.
Thorolf and his younger brother Egil (we read in the Saga)
kept away from Norway, where their enemy Eric was, and
offered their services to Athelstan, king of England.

EARLY in the reign of king Athelstan, Olaf, king of Scots, drew together a mighty host and marched upon England. When he came to Northumberland, the earls Alfgeir and Gudrek mustered their force and went against him. A battle was fought, wherein king Olaf won the victory, but earl Gudrek fell, and Alfgeir fled. And now king Olaf found no further resistance, but subdued all Northumberland.

Earl Alfgeir sought Athelstan and told him of his defeat. Athelstan sent word to his earls and nobles, and summoned forces; while himself with such power as he had marched against the Scots. But when it was noised abroad that Olaf had won a victory and subdued a large part of England, he soon had an army far exceeding that of Athelstan; for many nobles joined him. And Hring and Adils, two brothers, earls of Bretland, and tributaries under king Athelstan, went over to king Olaf.

Then was it resolved that Athelstan should go back to the south of England, and himself levy troops, coming northwards through the whole land. Over the army already assembled the king set as commanders the Icelanders, Thorolf and Egil, who had joined him a short while before with a strong force.   Earl Alfgeir was left in command of his own troops.

Messengers were now sent to king Olaf, saying that king Athelstan would fain enhazel him a field and offer battle on Vinheath by Vin-wood; meanwhile, they should forbear to harry his land: and of the twain he should rule England who should conquer in the battle.   He appointed a week hence for the con- flict; and whichever first came on the ground should wait a week for the other.   It was then the custom that, when a king had enhazelled a field, 'twas a shameful act to harry before the battle was ended. Accordingly king Olaf halted and harried not, but waited till the appointed day, when he moved his army to Vinheath.

North of the heath was a town.   There king Olaf quartered him with the greater part of his force.   But he sent men up to the heath: these were to take camping-ground and make all ready before the army. And when they came to the place, there stood all the hazel-poles set up to mark the ground where the battle should be.

To gain further time king Athelstan's men sent envoys to king Olaf about terms of peace.   Twice they went and returned: meantime forces flocked to

Athelstan's camp both day and night. But this was the counsel of wise men, to hide from Olaf the absence of Athelstan, and delay the battle till he should have come. When he came to the town that was close by the heath on the south, he at once sent messengers to king Olaf, saying: "Tell ye king Olaf that I will give him leave to go home to Scotland with all his forces; only let him restore what he has wrongfully taken here in the land. Then make we peace between us. But king Olaf shall be my vassal, and hold Scotland for me, and be my under-king." The messengers came to king Olaf about midnight. King Olaf and his men, on hearing this message, said all with one mouth that they must prepare for battle. And earl Adils spake: " Now methinks, O king, that has come to pass which I said, that ye would find tricksters in the English. We have sat here and waited long, while they have gathered forces. My counsel is, O king, that I and my brother at once ride forward this very night with our troop. It may be they will keep careless guard now that they know their king is near with a large army. So shall we dash upon them unawares: and if they turn and fly they will lose some men, and also be less bold afterwards for the main battle."

The king thought this good counsel. "We will

here make ready our army," said he, " as soon as it is light, and will move to support you."

So earl Hring and Adils his brother at once moved southwards for the heath. But when day dawned Thorolf's sentries saw the enemy approaching. Then was a war-blast blown, and men donned their arms. After that they drew up their force, making two divisions. Earl Alfgeir commanded one division, and the standard was borne before him. In that division were his own followers, and also what force had been gathered from the countryside. It was much larger than that of Thorolf and Egil.

Thorolf was thus armed. He had a shield ample and stout, a right strong helmet on his head; he was girded with the sword that he called Long,—a weapon large and good. In his hand he had a halberd, whereof the feather-formed blade was two ells long, ending in a four-edged spike; the blade was broad above, the socket both long and thick. The shaft stood just high enough for the hand to grasp the socket, and was remarkably thick. The socket fitted with iron prong on the shaft, which was also wound round with iron. Such weapons were called mail-piercers.

Egil was armed in the same way as Thorolf. He was girded with the sword that he called Adder; this he had gotten in Courland; it was a right good weapon. Neither of the two had shirt of mail.

They set up their standard, which was borne by Thorfid the Strong. All their men had Norwegian shields and Norwegian armour; and in their division were all the Norsemen who were present. Thorolf's force was drawn up near the wood; Alfgeir's moved along the river.

Earl Adils and his brother saw that they would not come upon Thorolf unawares, so they began to draw up their force. They also made two divisions, and had two standards. Adils was opposed to earl Alfgeir, Hring to the freebooters. The battle now began; both charged with spirit. Earl Adils pressed on hard and fast till Alfgeir gave ground; then Adils' men pressed on twice as boldly. Nor was it long before Alfgeir fled. And this is to be told of him, that he rode away south over the heath, and a company of men with him. He rode till he came to the town where sate king Athelstan.

Then spake the earl: "I deem it not safe for us to enter the town. We got sharp words of late when we came to the king after defeat by king Olaf; and he will not think our case bettered by this coming. No need to expect honour where he is."

So he rode to the south country, and of his travel 'tis to be told that he went night and day till he and his came westwards to Earlsness. There the earl got a ship to take him southwards over the sea; and he came to France, where half of his kin were. He never after returned to England.

Adils at first pursued the flying foe, but not far: then he turned back to where the battle was, and made an onset there. On seeing this, Thorolf said that Egil should turn and encounter him, and bade the standard be borne that way; his own men he bade hold well together and stand close.

"Move we to the wood," said he, "and let it cover our back, so that they may not come at us from all sides."

They did so; they followed along the wood. Fierce was the battle there. Egil charged against Adils, and they had a hard fight of it. The odds of numbers were great, yet more of Adils' men fell than of Egil's.

Then Thorolf became so furious that he cast his shield on his back, and grasping his halberd with both hands, bounded forward, dealing cut and thrust on either side. Men sprang from him both ways, but he slew many. Thus he cleared the way even to

earl Hring's standard, and then nothing could stop
him.   He slew the man who bore the earl's standard,
and cut down the standard-pole.   After that he lunged
with his halberd at the earl's breast, driving it right
through mail-coat and body, so that it came out at
the shoulders; and he lifted him up on the halberd
over his head, and planted the butt-end in the ground.
There on the weapon the earl breathed out his life
in sight of all, both friends and foes.   Then Thorolf
drew his sword and dealt blows on either side, his
men also charging.   Many Britons and Scots fell, but
some turned and fled.

But earl Adils, seeing his brother's fall, and the
slaughter of many of his force, and the flight of some,
while himself was in hard stress, turned to fly and ran
to the wood.   Into the wood fled he and his men:
but he had lowered his standard, so that none could
know his company from others.   And then all the
force that had followed the earl took to flight.
Thorolf and Egil pursued the flying foe.   Great was
then the slaughter: the fugitives were scattered far
and wide over the heath.

And soon the darkness of night begin to close in.
Thorolf and Egil returned to their camp: and just
then king Athelstan came up with the main army,

and they pitched their tents and made their arrangements.

A little after came king Olaf with his army: they, too, encamped and made their arrangements, where their men had before placed their tents. Then it was told king Olaf how both his earls Hring and Adils were fallen, and a multitude of his men likewise.

King Athelstan had passed the night before in the town whereof mention was made, and there he heard a rumour that there had been fighting on the heath. At once he and all the host made ready and marched northward to the heath. There they learnt all the tidings clearly, how that battle had gone. Then the brothers Thorolf and Egil came to meet the king. He thanked them much for their brave advance and for the victory they had won; he promised them his hearty friendship. They all remained together for the night.

No sooner did day dawn than Athelstan waked up his army. He held conference with his captains, and told them how his forces should be arranged. His own division he arranged first, and in the van thereof he set those companies that were the smartest.

These he said that Egil should command. "But Thorolf," said he, "shall be with his own men and

such others as I add thereto. This force shall be
opposed to that part of the enemy which is loose and
not in set array; for the Scots are ever loose in array,
they run to and fro, and dash forward here and there.
Often they prove dangerous if men be not wary, but
they are unsteady in the field if boldly faced."

Egil answered the king: "I will not that I and
Thorolf be parted in the battle: rather it seems to
me well that we two be placed together there where
is like to be most need and hardest fighting."

Thorolf said: "Leave we the king to rule where
he will place us; serve we him as he likes best. I
will, if you wish it, change places with you."

Egil said: "Brother, you must have your way;
but this separation I shall often rue."

After this they formed in the divisions as the king
had arranged, and the standards were raised. The
king's division stood on the plain towards the river;
Thorolf's division moved on the higher ground beside
the wood.

King Olaf drew up his forces when he saw king
Athelstan had done so. He also made two divisions;
and his own standard, and the division that himself
commanded he opposed to king Athelstan and his
division. Either had a large army, in numbers they

were well matched. And Olaf's second division
moved near the wood against the force under Thorolf,
the commanders thereof being Scotch earls, the men
mostly Scots; and it was a great multitude.

And now the armies closed, and the battle soon
waxed fierce. Thorolf pressed eagerly forward, caus-
ing his standard to be borne on along the woodside:
he thought to go so far forward as to turn upon the
Scotch king's division behind their shields. His own
men held their shields before them; they trusted to
the wood which was on their right to cover that side.
So far in advance went Thorolf that few of his men
were before him. But just when he was least on his
guard, out leapt from the wood earl Adils and his
followers. They thrust at Thorolf at once with many
halberds, and there by the wood he fell. But Thorfid,
who bore the standard, drew back to where the men
stood thicker. Adils now attacked them and a fierce
contest was there. The Scots shouted a shout of
victory, as having slain the enemy's chieftain.

This shout when Egil heard, and saw Thorolf's
standard going back, he felt sure that Thorolf himself
would not be with it. So he bounded thither over
the space between the two divisions. Full soon learnt
he tidings of what was done, when he came to his

men.   Then did he keenly spur them on to the charge,
himself foremost in the van.   He had in his hand his
sword Adder.   Forward Egil pressed, and hewed on
either hand of him, felling many men.   Thorfid bore
the standard close after him ; behind the standard
followed the rest.   Right sharp was the conflict there.
Egil went forward till he met earl Adils.   Few blows
did they exchange ere earl Adils fell, and many men
around him.   But after the earl's death his followers
fled.   Egil and his force pursued, and slew all whom
they overtook : no need there to beg quarter.   Nor
stood those Scotch earls long, when they saw the
others their fellows fly, but at once they took to their
heels.

Whereupon Egil and his men made or where king
Olaf's division was, and coming on them behind their
shields soon wrought great havoc.   The division
wavered and broke up.   Many of king Olaf's men
then fled, and the Norsemen shouted a shout of
victory.

But when king Athelstan perceived king Olaf's
division beginning to break, he spurred on his force
and bade his standard advance.   A fierce onset was
made, so that king Olaf's force recoiled, and there was
a great slaughter.   King Olaf fell there, and the greater

part of his forces, for of those who turned to fly all who were overtaken were slain.   Thus king Athelstan gained a signal victory.

While his men still pursued the fugitives, king Athelstan left the battle-field and rode back to the town, nor stayed he for the night before he came thither.   But Egil pursued the flying foe, and followed them far, slaying every man whom he overtook.

At length, sated with pursuit, he with his followers turned back, and came where the battle had been, and found there the dead body of his brother Thorolf. He took it up, washed it, and performed such other offices as were the wont of the time.   They dug a grave there, and laid Thorolf therein with all his weapons and raiment.   Then Egil clasped a gold bracelet on either wrist before he parted from him: this done, they heaped on stones and cast in mould. Then Egil sang a stave :

> " Dauntless the doughty champion
>   Dash'd on, the earl's bold slayer :
>   In stormy stress of battle
>   Stout-hearted Thorolf fell.
>   Green grows on soil of Vinheath
>   Grass o'er my noble brother ;
>   But we our woe—a sorrow
>   Worse than death-pang—must bear."

And again he further sang :

> " With warriors slain round standard
> The western field I burdened ;
> Adils with my blue Adder
> Assailed mid snow of war.
> Olaf, young prince, encountered
> England in battle-thunder :
> Hring stood not stour of weapons ;
> Not starved was raven's maw."

Then went Egil and those about him to seek king Athelstan, and at once they went before the king where he sat at the drinking.   There was much noise of merriment.   But when the king saw that Egil was come in, he bade the lower bench be cleared for them, and that Egil should sit in the high-seat facing the king.   Egil sat down there, and cast his shield before his feet.   He had his helm on his head, and laid his sword across his knees; and now and again he half drew it, then clashed it back into the sheath.   He sat upright, but with head bent forward.

Egil was large-featured, broad of forehead, with large eyebrows, a nose not long but very thick, lips wide and long, chin exceeding broad, as was all about the jaws; thick-necked was he, and big-shouldered beyond other men, hard-featured, and grim when angry.   He was well-made, more than commonly

tall, had hair wolf-gray and thick, but became early
bald. He was black-eyed and brown-skinned.

As he sat there, he drew one eyebrow down towards
the cheek, the other up to the roots of the hair. He
would not drink now, though the horn was borne to
him, but alternately twitched his brows up and down.
King Athelstan sat in the upper high-seat. He, too,
had laid his sword across his knees. When they had
sat there for a time, then the king drew his sword
from the sheath, and took from his arm a gold ring
large and good, and placing it upon the sword-point
he stood up, and went across the floor, and reached
it over the fire to Egil. Egil stood up, and unsheathed
his sword, and went across the floor. The sword-
point he stuck within the round of the ring, and drew
it to him; then went he back to his place. The king
sate him again on his high-seat. But when Egil was
set down he drew the ring on his arm, and now his
eyebrows went back to their place. Then he laid
down sword and helm, took the horn that they bare to
him, and drank it off. Thereafter sang he:

> "Mailed monarch, god of battle,
> Maketh the tinkling circlet
> Hang, his own arm forsaking,
> 　On hawk-trod wrist of mine.

I bear on arm brand-wielding
Bracelet of red gold gladly.
War-falcon's feeder meetly
   Findeth such meed of praise."

After this Egil drank his share and talked with others.   Presently the king bade two chests be borne in ; two men bare each ; both were full of silver.

The king said : "These chests, Egil, thou shalt have ; and, if thou comest to Iceland, shalt carry this money to thy father : as payment for a son I send it to him ; but some of it thou shalt divide among such kinsmen of thyself and Thorolf as thou thinkest most honourable.   But for thyself thou shalt take payment for a brother, biding here with me, lands or chattels, which thou wilt.   And if thou wilt abide with me long, I will give thee honour and dignity such as thyself mayest name."

Egil took the money, and thanked the king for his gifts and friendly words.   Thenceforward Egil began to be cheerful.

Then those men were healed whose wounds gave hope of life.   Egil abode with Athelstan for the next winter after Thorolf's death, and had very great honour from the king.

FROM THE STORY OF GUNN-LAUG SNAKE-TONGUE.

Although in some points this Saga is not historically correct, it is a very good one, in style, in the interest of the plot, which is skilfully worked out. It has been translated by Magnusson and Morris : I had translated it before I had read (or I believe, knew of) their version : a portion of it I here give ; and some scenes of it I have rendered as ballads, which will be found later on. Magnusson and Morris have well termed it "an Icelandic love-story." If it is a romance, it is a well-written one.

THORSTEIN'S DREAM. THE BIRTH AND FOSTERING OF HELGA THE FAIR.

THERE was a man named Thorstein, the son of Egil Skallagrimsson. He dwelt at Borg on Borgar Firth : wealthy was he in possessions, a great chieftain, gentle-minded, just in all things. In stature and strength he was not of such prowess as his father Egil, yet he was a man of much mark and generally liked. He was handsome, white-haired, with very beautiful eyes. He had to wife Jofridr, the daughter of Gunnar Hlif's son. Jofridr was a woman of a noble spirit: she and Thorstein had many children, but few of them come into this story.

'Tis told that one summer a ship came off the sea into the mouth of Gufu river: the skipper's name was Bergfinn, he was a Norwegian by birth, wealthy, well-stricken in years, a wise man. It was Thorstein's wont to ride down to the incoming ships and to arrange about the market of the wares: and so did he now. The Easterlings found for themselves lodging, but Thorstein, at his request, received the skipper into his house. During the winter Bergfinn showed himself a man of few words, though Thorstein treated him well. The Easterling took much pleasure in dreams.

One day in the spring Thorstein asked Bergfinn if he would ride up with him under Valfell. The Thing-field of the Borgarfirthers was there; and Thorstein had been told that the walls of his booth were fallen. The Easterling readily agreed to go, and they rode away next day a party of three, with some house-carles of Thorstein's, till they came up under Valfell to a house called Grenjar, where dwelt a poor man named Atli, a tenant of Thorstein. Him Thorstein asked to go with them to the work, bringing spade and shovel; he did so.

And when they came to the booth-toft, they all set to work and built up the walls. The weather was hot and sunny, and Thorstein and the Easterling became wearied; and when they had built up the walls, then they two sate them down in the booth-toft; and Thorstein slept and was uneasy in his sleep. The Easterling sate by him and let him dream his dream out; and when he awoke he was exhausted. The Easterling asked what he had dreamt to make his sleep so uneasy.

Thorstein answered, "There is nothing in dreams!"

But as they rode home that evening, the Easterling asked again what Thorstein had dreamt.

Thorstein said, "If I tell you the dream, you shall interpret for me what it means."

The Easterling promised that he would try to do so.

Then said Thorstein: "This I dreamed, that methought I was at home at Borg, and was outside before the men's door; and I looked up at the house-top, and lo, on the ridge a swan, beautiful and bright; it was, methought, mine own, and I prized it well. Then saw I fly down from the fell a large eagle; he flew thither and perched beside the swan and chattered blithely to her, and methought she was well pleased thereat. This I saw, that the eagle had black eyes and iron claws; a brave fellow he seemed.

"Next I saw another bird fly from the south; he flew thither to Borg, and perched on the house beside the swan and would fain win her love. This, too, was a large eagle. But soon methought that eagle, who was first there, was much angered at the other's coming; and the twain fought fiercely and long, and, as I could see, both of them were bleeding, and the end of their conflict was that they fell back one on either side from the roof-ridge, and both were dead. But the swan sate there still drooping and downcast. And then I saw a bird fly out of the west, it was a falcon; it perched beside the swan and made friends with her, and after that they twain flew away together to the same quarter of the heavens. And with that I awoke."

"But this dream," said Thorstein, "is of no import: and maybe 'tis because of winds meeting aloft, from those quarters whence the birds seemed to fly."

The Easterling said: "That is not my mind, that it is so."

Said Thorstein, "Make of the dream what you deem most likely, and let me hear."

Then said the Easterling: "Those birds will be fetches of men. Your wife is with child: she will bear a girl comely and fair, whom you will love much; and noble suitors will woo her from those quarters of the heavens whence the eagles appeared to fly. And they will love her passionately and fight about her, and both will die for this cause. And after that a third suitor will come from the quarter whence flew the falcon, and to him she will be given in marriage. Now have I interpreted your dream as I think it will turn out."

Thorstein answered: "The dream is ill-explained and in unfriendly wise: and 'tis certain you have no skill in explaining dreams."

Said the Easterling: "Hereof you will find proof by how it turns out."

Thorstein was henceforward cool to the Easterling, who in the summer went away, and is now out of the story.

In the summer Thorstein made him ready to go to the Thing, and spake thus to Jofridr his wife ere he left home.

"You are," he said, "with child; now this child shall be exposed, if you bear a girl, but reared, if you bear a boy."

It was then a custom sometimes, when the land was altogether heathen, that poor men, who had

many helpless ones to provide for, had their children
exposed; this was, however, thought an ill-deed.

And when Thorstein had spoken thus, Jofridr
answered: "These words are unlike you, such a man
as you are; it beseems you not to have such a thing
done, and you so wealthy."

Thorstein answered: "You know my temper, that
it will not be well for you if you disobey me."

Then he rode to the Thing: and Jofridr, while he
was away, bare a very beautiful girl. The women
would fain bring it to her; but she said there was
little need of this, and she bade them summon her
shepherd who was named Thorvard, to whom she said:

"Take my horse and saddle it, and carry this child
westwards to Thorgerdr Egil's daughter: bid her rear
it privily, so that Thorstein know naught thereof.
Such eyes of love do I turn on this child, that I cannot bear to have it exposed. But here are three marks
of silver, which you shall have for your wage; and
Thorgerdr will find you a passage westwards and means
for the sea voyage."

Thorvard did as she bade: he rode west to Hjardarholt with the child, and gave it into Thorgerdr's hands:
but she had it reared by a tenant of hers who dwelt
further in at Leysingstead on Hvammsfirth. And she

found Thorvard a passage northwards to Skeljavik on Steingrims firth, and means for the sea voyage: so thence he went abroad, and is now out of the story.

When Thorstein came home from the Thing, Jofridr told him that the child had been exposed as he had bidden, but that the shepherd had run away and stolen her horse. Thorstein said she had done well, and got him another shepherd. And now six years passed without this being known.

Then Thorstein rode west to Hjardarholt to visit Olaf Peacock, his brother-in-law, Hauskuld's son, who was held most in honour of all the chieftains there in the west. Thorstein was well received there, as was natural. And one day at a feast, so 'tis said, Thorgerdr sat talking with Thorstein her brother on the upper bench, while Olaf was talking with other men. But on the bench over against them sate three girls.

Then said Thorgerdr: "Brother, how like you those three lasses who sit over against us?"

He answered: "Right well. But one is far the most beautiful. And she has the comeliness of Olaf, but the fair hue and look of us Moormen."

Said Thorgerdr: "True indeed, brother, is what you say, that she has the fair hue and look of us Moormen, but not the comeliness of Olaf Peacock, for she is not his daughter."

"How can that be," said Thorstein, "when she is your daughter?"

She answered: "To tell you the truth, kinsman, she is your daughter, not mine, this fair maid." And then she told him all that had happened, and begged him to forgive her and his wife this disobedience.

Thorstein said: "I cannot blame you two in this: things turn out mostly as by fate they must: and you have well made amends for my foolishness. So pleased am I with this maid, that I think me most fortunate to own so beautiful a child. What is her name?"

"Helga is her name," said Thorgerdr.

"Helga the fair," said Thorstein. "And now shall you arrange for her to go home with me."

She did so. Thorstein was sped on his way with good gifts; and Helga rode home with him; and was brought up and bred there with much honour and love of father and mother and all her kin.

GUNNLAUG'S EARLY YEARS

At Gillsbank on White-river-side dwelt Illugi Swarthy son of Hallkel: whose mother was Thuridr

Dylla, daughter of Gunnlaug Snake-tongue. He and his wife Ingibjorg had among other children one named Gunnlaug. Gunnlaug came early to manhood, was tall and strong, had light chestnut hair of luxuriant growth, a somewhat unsightly nose, was slim-waisted, broad-shouldered, well-built, was boastful, ambitious from his earliest years, unyielding, resolute, a good poet, biting in words; he was called Gunnlaug Snake-tongue.

Now when Gunnlaug was fifteen years old, he asked his father to fit him out for a journey, saying that he would fain go abroad and see other men's manners. Goodman Illugi refused, saying that he did not think him fit for foreign lands, when he could hardly manage him as he would there at home.

But one morning, a little after this, Illugi went out early, and saw that his outhouse was opened, and there were laid out some packs of wares, six, and saddle-pads therewith. At this he wondered much.

Then came out some one leading four horses: it was his son Gunnlaug; who said, "I laid out the packs."

Illugi asked why he had done this. He said that these should be his outfit.

Illugi said, " You shall not slight my authority, and

nowhither shall you go." And he dragged the packs in again.

Gunnlaug then rode away and came that evening down to Borg, and goodman Thorstein asked him to stay there, which offer he accepted. Gunnlaug told Thorstein what had passed between him and his father. Thorstein bade him bide there for such time as he would; and he was there for that year, and learnt law-wisdom from Thorstein, and won much honour of all men there.

The two, Helga and Gunnlaug, were often playing draughts together: they soon took a liking for one another, as was afterwards proved. They were much of an age. Helga was so beautiful that learned men say she was the most beautiful woman ever seen in Iceland. Her hair was so long that it could veil her whole body, and it was bright as beaten gold: nor was there any match like Helga the fair in Borgarfirth and the whole country-side.

And one day, while men sate in the common room at Borg, Gunnlaug said to Thorstein, "There is one thing in law which you have not taught me, how to betroth me a wife."

Thorstein said, "That is a simple matter," and taught him the procedure.

Then said Gunnlaug, " Now you shall see whether I have understood this. I will take your hand and make as if I betrothed to me Helga, your daughter."

" That, I think, is needless," said Thorstein.

But at once Gunnlaug grasped his hand and said, " Grant me this."

" Do as you will," said Thorstein ; " but they who are present are to know that this shall be as if unsaid, and no trickery shall follow."

Then Gunnlaug named him witnesses, and betrothed to him Helga, and afterwards asked whether that would stand good so.

Thorstein said that it would. And those who were present were much amused at the jest.

OF HRAFN AND HIS TRAVELS ; OF GUNN- LAUG'S JOURNEYINGS ; GUNNLAUG AND HRAFN QUARREL

There was a man named Hrafn, a young man at the same time with Gunnlaug : he was son of Onund of Mossfell. He was tall, strong, handsome, and a good poet. When he was grown to manhood he travelled from land to land, and was well liked wherever he came.

Gunnlaug Snake-tongue (as before said) was for some time at Borg : then afterwards he spent part of his time at Borg with Thorstein, part with Illugi his father ; and so passed three years. He was now eighteen years old, and there was better agreement between father and son. Gunnlaug a second time asked his father for an outfit. Illugi said, "It shall be as you wish ; you have mended your manners from what they were." And he rode out and bought for Gunnlaug the half share of a ship laid up in the mouth of Gufu river. For which Gunnlaug thanked him much.

While the wares were being carried to the ship, and the ship was being made ready, Gunnlaug was at Borg, and he found it more pleasant to talk with Helga, than to be at work with the chapmen.

And one day, when he was with Thorstein, he asked him plainly to give him Helga the fair, his daughter. Thorstein at first said that this was non-sense : then that it was no equal match between him and Helga, while he was so unsettled. Many words passed between the twain : but Thorstein would not accept Gunnlaug. Then Gunnlaug, with Illugi his father, made in form an offer for Thorstein's daughter Helga ; and the end was that Thorstein for his friend-ship with Illugi, consented that Helga should be promised wife to Gunnlaug, but not betrothed; and that she should wait three winters: but Gunnlaug should go abroad. After that, if Gunnlaug came not to Iceland, or did not satisfy Thorstein in character, the bargain should be off.

And with that they parted. Illugi rode home, Gunnlaug to the ship. And when they got a wind, they put out to sea, and came to Norway, and sailed by Thrandheim to Nidaros, where they lay at anchorage and put out their cargo.

At that time the rulers in Norway were earl Eric, Hacon's son, and Svein his brother. Earl Eric had his residence at Hladir on his father's estate; he was a powerful chief. Skuli, Thorstein's son, was then with the earl, being one of his bodyguard and well-esteemed.

It is told that Gunnlaug and Audun went with five more up to Hladir. Gunnlaug was thus drest: he had on a grey kirtle and white stocking-breeks. He had a boil on the instep of his foot, whence was discharged blood and matter as he walked. In this dress he went before the earl, and with him Audun; and they saluted the earl courteously. The earl knew Audun, and asked tidings of Iceland; and Audun told him what there was to tell.

The earl asked Gunnlaug who he was; and he told him his name and family.

"Skuli, Thorstein's son," said the earl; "of what men comes he in Iceland?"

"Sire," said Skuli, "receive him well; he is son of a most distinguished man in Iceland, Illugi Swarthy of Gillsbank, and he is my foster-brother."

Then said the earl, "What ails thy foot, Icelander?"

"A boil is on it, sire," said he.

"And yet thou walkest not lame," said the earl.

Gunnlaug answered, "No need to walk lame, while both legs are of one length."

Then spoke a man of the earl's guard, who was named Thorir: "This Icelander struts proudly; 'twere well we put him to some proof."

Gunnlaug looked at him and said:

> "There guards your Grace
> One false and base.
> Trust him not lightly,
> Black and unsightly."

Then Thorir would fain have gripped his axe. But the earl said, "Let be; men should not heed such things. But how old art thou, Icelander?"

Gunnlaug answered, "I am now eighteen years old, sire."

"This I would warrant," said the earl, "that thou wilt not live another eighteen."

Gunnlaug said, but very low, "Pray no evil for me, but pray for thyself, rather."

Said the earl, "What art thou saying now, Icelander?"

Gunnlaug answered, "What I thought to be right, that thou shouldest pray no evil for me, but pray a better lot for thyself."

"How so?" said the earl.

"That thou come not by the same death as did earl Hacon, thy father."

The earl turned red as blood, and bade them seize at once this fool. Then went Skuli before the earl, and said, "Do as I entreat, sire, spare the man's life, but let him go hence forthwith."

The earl said, "Let him begone at once, if he will have life, and come never more into my realm."

Then Skuli went out with Gunnlaug, and down to the landing-stage. There lay a ship bound for England, ready to put out; in which Skuli took a passage for Gunnlaug and his kinsman Thorkel. But Gunnlaug gave into Audun's keeping his ship and such wares as he took not with him. And now Gunnlaug and his shipmates sailed to the English sea, and came

in the autumn south to London Bridge, and there
set up their ship on rollers.

At that time Ethelred, son of Edgar, ruled England
as king: he was a good ruler; he resided for the
winter in London town.   Gunnlaug forthwith went
before the king and greeted him well and worthily.
The king asked of what land he were: Gunnlaug told
him.   "And," said he, " I have sought thee, sire, for
this reason, that I have made a poem about thee, and
I would have thee grant it a hearing."   The king
said this thould be so; and Gunnlaug recited the
poem well and boldly: and this is the burden thereof:

> "England's great-souled king
> As a god all fear:
> Ethelred high chiefs
> And low churls obey."

The king thanked him for the poem, and gave him
as poet's meed a scarlet cloak, made of the best skins,
and lace-trimmed down to the skirt.   He made him
also one of his guard: and Gunnlaug was with the
king that winter and held in much honour.

And one day, early in the morning, Gunnlaug met
three men in a street, and their leader was named
Thororm.   He was tall and strong, a right dangerous
fellow to encounter.

He said, " Northman, lend me some money."

Gunnlaug answered, "That would be unwise, to lend one's money to unknown men."

He answered, "I shall pay you back on the appointed day."

"Then will I risk it," said Gunnlaug.   And he gave him the money.

Soon afterwards Gunnlaug met the king and told him of the loan.

The king said, "'Tis ill done; this fellow is a robber and evildoer; have no dealings with him: but I will make up to thee the sum of money."

Gunnlaug answered, "Ill fares it then with us thy guards; we attack guiltless men, while we let such as he is hold what is ours: that shall never be."

And soon after this he met Thororm, and demanded of him the money; but he said he should not pay. Gunnlaug then spoke this stave:

> "Lord of clashing falchions,
>   Foolishly thou filchest
>   Wealth, and me a warrior
>   Trickest with thy wiles.
>   Know, not vain my nickname,
>   Fitting well my nature;
>   As a child I took it,
>   I am Adder-tongue."

"Now will I offer thee these terms," said Gunn-
lau3: "Either pay me my money, or do battle with
me three days hence."

Then laughed the robber and said: "None before
you has ever dared to challenge me to combat, though
many have suffered loss from me: but I am quite
ready for this same." And with that they parted for
the time.

Gunnlaug told the king what had been done.

The king said, "Now has this come to be a most
desperate case. This man blunts every weapon.
Thou shalt follow my counsel: here is a sword that
I will give thee; with this thou must fight, but
show him another." Gunnlaug thanked the king
much.

And when they were ready for combat, Thororm
asked which was the sword he used. Gunnlaug
showed him a sword and brandished it, but the sword
given him by the king hung by a loop round the hilt
drawn over his arm. The Berserk said when he saw
the sword, "I do not fear that sword." And he
hewed at Gunnlaug with his sword and almost cut all
his shield away. Gunnlaug in return hewed at him
with the king's gift: but the Berserk stood uncovered
before him, thinking that Gunnlaug wielded the same

sword that he had showed: and so Gunnlaug dealt him his death-blow.

The king thanked him for this work, and hereby gat he great glory in England and far and wide elsewhere.

In the spring, when ships began to go from land to land, Gunnlaug asked leave of king Ethelred to sail somewhither. The king asked what he wanted to do this for. Gunnlaug answered, "I would fain fulfil what I have purposed and vowed." And he recited this stave:

> "Thus runneth my vow,
>   To voyage and visit
>   In court and in castle
>   Three kings and two earls.
>   Then back turn I hither,
>   When he calls me to battle
>   Who giveth gold arm-rings,
>   The rich king's great heir."

"So shall it be," saith the king, and gave him a gold ring weighing six ounces; "but thou shalt promise me this," said the king, "to come back to me next autumn; for thy skill and prowess makes me loth to lose thee."

GUNNLAUG IN IRELAND AND THE ORKNEYS

THEN Gunnlaug sailed from England with some chapmen northwards to Dublin. King Sigtrygg Silkbeard then ruled Ireland; son he was of Olaf Kvaran and Kormlad his queen: he had then but a short while held the kingdom.

Gunnlaug went before the king and greeted him well and worthily. The king received him with honour. Gunnlaug said, " I have composed a poem about thee, and would gain a hearing."

The king answered, "No man ere now hath brought me a poem: surely I will hear it."

Gunnlaug then recited the epic; and this is the burden :

> " Wolf, the witch's steed,
> Sigtrygg with flesh doth feed."

This also is in the poem :

> " Words full wise I know,
> Well can praise bestow :
> Kvaran's son, a king,
> Seed of kings, I sing."

> " Monarch frank and free
> (I as bard foresee)
> For my guerdon fair
> Gold ring will not spare.

Honour'd prince, now say,
Heard'st thou ever lay
Thy renown rehearse
In a nobler verse?"

The king thanked him for the poem, and called his treasurer and said, "How should I reward the poem?"

He answered, "What wilt thou, sire?"

"How were it rewarded," said the king; "should I give him two ships of burden?"

The treasurer answered: "That is too much, sire. Other kings give as poet's meed valuable treasures, such as a good sword, or a good gold ring."

The king gave him his suit of raiment new-made of scarlet; a lace-trimmed kirtle, and cloak of valuable skins, and withal a gold ring weighing a mark. Gunnlaug thanked him, and remained there a short time; thence he went to the Orkneys.

At that time the ruler in the Orkneys was earl Sigurd, Hlodver's son: he was friendly to Icelanders. Gunnlaug greeted the earl well, and said he had a poem to bring before him. The earl said he would hear his poem, knowing that he came of great men in Iceland. Gunnlaug recited his poem; it was a short ode, well composed. The earl gave him a broad-axe all overlaid with silver as poet's meed, and asked him to stay at his court.

Gunnlaug thanked him for the gift and for the offer, but said he must go east to Sweden : and soon after he took ship with some chapmen sailing to Norway; and they came in the autumn east to King's-Stone. Thorkel, his kinsman, was his companion all this time. From King's-Stone they got them guides up to western Gautland, and came on to the trading-town named Skarar.

There ruled an earl named Sigurd; he was well stricken in years. Gunnlaug went before him, and said he had made a poem about him. The earl gave it a good hearing. Gunnlaug recited the poem; it was a short ode. The earl thanked him and rewarded him, and asked him to remain there for the winter. Earl Sigurd held a great Yule-feast in the winter. And on the eve of Yule there came thither from the north out of Norway messengers of earl Eric, twelve men in company, bringing gifts to earl Sigurd.

The earl received them well and on Yule day placed them next to Gunnlaug. There was much ale-mirth. The Gauts talked how there was no earl greater or more famous than Sigurd : the Norsemen thought earl Eric far before him. And about this they wrangled, and chose Gunnlaug as umpire between them on the matter. Gunnlaug then recited this stave:

> "Of this earl, spear-maidens,
> Speak ye forth the glory:
> He hath seen wave-ridges,
> Hoary warrior he.
> Eric bold, beholding
> Crested billows eastwards,
> On sea-steed victorious
> Battle-tide hath stemm'd."

Both liked the decision well, but the Norsemen were the better pleased. The messengers went back thence after Yule with rich gifts, which earl Sigurd sent to earl Eric. They told earl Eric of Gunnlaug's decision. The earl thought that Gunnlaug had showed towards himself frankness and friendship; and he let it be known that Gunnlaug might revisit his realm in peace. Gunnlaug afterwards learnt what the earl had said.

Earl Sigurd gave Gunnlaug, at his request, guides eastwards to Tiundaland in Sweden.

IN SWEDEN GUNNLAUG MEETS HRAFN

At that time there ruled in Sweden king Olaf the Swede, son of king Eric the victorious and Sigridr the proud, daughter she of Skogla-Tosti. He was a powerful and renowned king, and very ambitious. Gunnlaug came to Upsala in the spring, when the Swedes' Thing was being holden; and so soon as he could approach the king he saluted him. The king received him well, and asked him who he was. Gunnlaug answered that he was an Icelander. The king said, "Hrafn, of what men in Iceland comes he?" A man stood up from the lower bench, tall and stalwart; he came near the king and said, "Sire, he is of the best family, and himself a right doughty man."

"Let him go then and sit by thee," said the king.

Said Gunnlaug, "I have a poem to bring thee, and I would fain have thee grant it a hearing and silence."

"Go first, and sit ye down both," said the king; "we have no leisure now to spend over poems." They did so.

Then Gunnlaug and Hrafn fell to talking together; each told the other of his travels. Hrafn said he had left Iceland the summer before for Norway, and in the beginning of the winter had come eastwards to Sweden. They soon got on well together.

And one day, when the Thing was ended, these two, Gunnlaug and Hrafn, were both before the king.

Then said Gunnlaug, "Now would I fain, sire, that thou shouldst hear my poem."

"That may well be so now," said the king.

"I, too, would fain recite my poem, sire," said Hrafn.

"That may well be done," said the king.

"Then I will recite my poem first, sire," said Gunnlaug, "if thou wilt have it so."

"I ought first to recite, sire," said Hrafn, "for I first came to thee."

Gunnlaug said: "Where came ever our fathers, so that my father was stern-boat to thine? Where but nowhere? And so shall it be with us twain."

Hrafn answered, "Show we then courtesy, and bring not this matter to wrangling, but let the king decide."

The king said: "Gunnlaug shall recite first, for he is ill-humoured if he get not his will."

Then Gunnlaug recited the epic that he had composed about king Olaf; and when the epic was ended, then said the king: "Hrafn," said he, "how is the poem composed?"

"Right well, sire," said he; "'tis a big-worded poem, but uncouth and somewhat stiff in form, as is Gunnlaug himself in mood."

"Now shalt thou recite thy poem, Hrafn," said the king. He did so. And when it was ended, then said the king: "Gunnlaug," said he, "how is this poem composed?"

Gunnlaug answered: "Right well, sire," said he; "'tis a pretty poem, as is Hrafn himself to look upon, but petty in appearance."

"But wherefore, Hrafn," said he, "did you compose a mere ode about the king? did you not think him worthy of an epic?"

Hrafn answered: "Speak we no more of this: we may take it up again later." And with that they parted.

A little after this Hrafn was made one of king Olaf's guard; and he asked his leave to go abroad, which the king granted. And when Hrafn was ready to start, he spoke thus to Gunnlaug: "Now shall our friendship end; seeing that you wished to shame me here before the chief men: now will I on every occasion work your dishonour no less than you have here sought mine."

Gunnlaug answered: "I fear not your threats: nowhere shall we twain come that I be less honoured than you."

FROM THE STORY OF THE WATERDALESMEN

This Saga begins in Norway, before the time of Harold Fairhair: then the family concerned move to Iceland, and settle in the north of Iceland.

EARLY ADVENTURES OF THORSTEIN, KETILL'S SON

THERE was a man named Ketill, nicknamed Raum; he was a mighty man: he lived at the homestead called Raumsdale, northwards in Norway. He was the son of Orm Shell-sherd, who was the son of Horse-bjorn, the son of Raum from North Norway. At the time when this story begins there were shire-kings in Norway. Ketill was a famous man, and a wealthy, strong of body, right doughty in all dangers: he had been employed in warfare for the earlier part of his life, but now, as age came over him, he sat in his homestead.

He had to wife Mjöll, the daughter of Anir Bow-swayer.   Ketill and she had a son named Thorstein, goodly to look upon, but of no great mark for stature or strength, who was eighteen years old when the events of this story began.   Yet for conduct and all capacity Thorstein was up to a high standard among the young men then living.

At that time it came to be known that there must be robbers or evil-doers on the road lying between Jamtaland and Raumsdale; for none came back who went that way: yea, even though fifteen or twenty went together, yet had none come back, so men were pretty sure that someone of remarkable prowess must lie out there.   The men of Ketill the yeoman suffered least from these attacks, both in manslayings and loss of property: but people made much talk about it in the way of blame, saying that 'twas a poor sort of man they had now for chief of the district, when no steps were taken against such outrages: Ketill, they said, was now very old.

Ketill, though he did not openly show that he heeded this much, yet thought on what they said. And so it was that one day Ketill spake thus to Thorstein his son :

" The ways of young men are become other now

than they were when I was young. Then men
desired exploits of some kind : either to undertake
warfare, or to gather wealth and honour by such
actions as have some danger. But now young men
are content to coddle themselves at home, and sit
stewing over the fire, and fill their bellies with mead
and beer, while manhood and hardihood wane. I
gathered wealth and honour by daring to face danger
and hard combat. You now, Thorstein, have little
share of bodily strength and stature, and 'tis most
likely that you will follow your own ways, and as to
energy and all daring will go on as you do ; for you
have no wish to imitate the deeds of your former kin ;
what you look like, that you show yourself to be ;
mind will follow body. Once it was the wont of
mighty men, kings or earls, our equals, to go a-war-
ring, and gather riches and renown. And such
wealth was not to reckon as heritage, nor was a son
to take it after a father, rather it was to lie in the
burial mound by the men themselves. And though
the sons should take their father's lands, yet would
they never maintain themselves in their quality,
(though inheriting their rank) unless they exposed
themselves and their men to risk and battle : winning
so for themselves wealth and worship, each in his turn,

and following in the footsteps of their kin.   But you, I think, know nothing of warriors' law : and yet I could teach it to you, for you are now of that age when 'tis time for you to put your fortune to the proof."

Thorstein answered : "I am now egged on, if that boots aught."   And he rose and went out in great anger.

A large wood lay between Raumsdale and Upland, through which ran a public road, now made impassable by those evil wights believed to lie out there, though none could tell of them.   And it was thought that it would be a great exploit to remedy this mischief.

Shortly after father and son had thus talked together, Thorstein went out alone from the drinking ; and he thought this the best course for him to put his father's fortune to proof, and no more be a mark for his bitter words : rather would he now encounter some danger.

So he took his horse and rode alone to the wood where he thought there was most likelihood of evil deeds, though he deemed that he had little chance of success, against such odds of strength as would be there : but now he felt he would rather lay down his life than go out for nothing.   He tethered his horse by the wood, and then went into it, and found a by-path leading off the high road, and, when he had gone a long way, he found in the wood a large well-built house. This harbourage, Thorstein felt sure, would belong to the infesters of the highway, whether one or more. Then Thorstein went into the hall and found there large chests and many good things. There was a great pile of firewood, but on the other side wares in sacks, and stuffs of all kinds. There too he saw a bed; far larger was it than any that Thorstein had ever seen before: a mighty big man, thought he, must it be who matched so roomy a bed. The bed had rich hangings. A table was there spread with clean cloth and sumptuous dainties and the best drink. Thorstein did not touch these things.

Then he sought some device that he might not be seen at once by him who dwelt in the house, because he would like to know how matters stood, before they came to speech or saw each other. So he got up on to the pile of wares among the sacks and sat there. Soon, as evening came on, he heard outside a great noise; and presently a man came in leading a horse: the man was very big, with white hair that fell over his shoulders with fair curls. To Thorstein he seemed very handsome. Soon he stirred up the fire before him, having first led his horse to a stall; he set a basin before him, and washed his hands, and dried them with a white napkin. He also poured out from a cask excellent drink into a large goblet, and then began his meal. All the behaviour of this man seemed to Thorstein remarkable and very well-mannered. He was of far larger stature than Thorstein's father, Ketill, indeed he was, as Thorstein thought, an exceedingly big man.

And when the dweller in the house had ended his meat, he sat down by the fire, and looked at it and said: "Some change has been made here; the fire is more burnt out than I thought; I fancy it has been stirred lately. I do not know what that means; maybe men are come who lie in wait for my life; nor for that lack they cause: I must go and search round the house." Then he took a fire-brand, and searched, and came where the heap of wares was. It was so arranged that from the pile one could get to the chimney that was over the hall. And when the robber came to search the pile, Thorstein was out of it, and the robber found him not, for Thorstein's destined lot was other than to be slain there. Three times did the man search round the house, but he found nothing.

Then said the man of the house: "I will now let things be quiet; 'tis uncertain how things may turn out; it may be that in my case the proverb will prove true, 'Ill rede ends ill.'" He then went back to the bed, and laid aside his sword. This appeared to Thorstein to be a most valuable weapon, and likely to be a good biter: and it occurred to him that it would be well if he could get this. Also it came into his mind that his father had said he was no better at a weapon than his daughter or any other woman, and that more honour would come to his kin were there a gap in their family, than a man such as he.

Such thoughts whetted Thorstein on, and he sought now some means by which he could redress the great wrong done, though on the other hand it seemed to him that there would be a great loss in this man. Soon the robber went to sleep; but Thorstein made trial with some noise, how sound asleep he was; he awoke at the noise, and turned himself: then after a time Thorstein made another trial, at which he awoke again, but less. The third time Thorstein came forth, and struck a strong blow on the bed-post, but found that all was quiet around him. Then Thorstein stirred up a flame, and went to the bed to see whether the man was still there. He saw that he lay there, sleeping in a silken shirt broidered with gold, and with face upturned. Then Thorstein brandished the sword and thrust at the breast of the big man, giving him a deep wound. Sharply he turned, gripped Thorstein, and snatched him up on to the bed beside him, but the sword stood in the wound. And so hard had Thorstein smitten, that the point was fixed in the bed. But the man was of fearsome strength, and he let the sword stand there as it was, while Thorstein lay between him and the wainscoting.

Then spake the wounded man: "Who is he that has dealt me a blow?"

The other answered: "I am named Thorstein, and I am the son of Ketill Raum."

Said the man: "Methinks I knew your name before: yet deem I that this has been least deserved from you and your father, for I have done you little or no harm. But now you were rather too soon, and I rather too late, for even now I was ready to go abroad, and turn from this my evil course. Now have I free choice with you, whether I let you live or die. If I do after your deserving, and what you have exposed yourself to, no one would then tell of our dealings; but I think it wisest now to grant you your life, for thus I may have good from you if it shall so hap. And now I also will tell you my name; it is Jökull, and I am the son of Ingimund, earl of Gautland; and after the manner of great men's sons, I gathered me wealth, though by rather rough work, and I was even now preparing to go abroad.

But if you think the gift of your life any boon, then go you to my father; but first get speech of my mother, who is named Vigdis, and tell her alone of this hap, and bear to her my loving greeting, and say that she is to bring you into peace with the Earl, and full friendship, in such wise, that he give you to wife his daughter, my sister, who is named Thordis.

Here now is a gold token which you shall bear to show that I send you. And, though her grief for the loss of me will be great, yet I expect that my mother will weigh more my love and message than your deserving; and my mind tells me that you are to be a lucky man. And if it be your destiny to have sons, and your sons have issue, then let not my name die forgotten. 'Tis in this that I hope for good, and this shall I have for the gift to thee of life."

Thorstein bade him do as he pleased about this gift of life and other things; he would, he said, beg for nothing. Jökull said that Thorstein's life was in his hands. "But," said he, "you have been sorely egged on

to this by your father; and now his counsel has keenly
bitten me, and I see that you would be content we should
both die; but a greater destiny is in store for you:
in the matter of courage and manliness, they will not
lack a leader where you bear rule.   And for my sister's
marriage, 'tis a better provision that you take her to
wife, than that Vikings take her as prize of war.
Further, though it be offered to you to remain in
Gautland, go you rather to your own possessions.
For my father's kin will not allow of your rule after
his death; but it may be that there will be grievous
fighting in your families, and men will lose guiltless
kinsfolk.   And do not you speak of my name pub-
licly, save to your father and my kinsfolk; for my
life has taken the wrong way, and thus is rewarded
worthily, even as it fares with most wrongdoers.
Now take and keep this gold for a token; but pluck
out the sword, and then our talk together will not be
long."

Then Thorstein plucked out the sword, and Jökull
died.

After these doings Thorstein rode home.   And as
he came near the farm-buildings, he saw many men
riding to meet him, among whom he recognised his
father, and many of his acquaintance, and they were

all going to search for him. But when they met, Ketill greeted his son with joyful words, as one whom he had recovered from the grave, and he said : " I repented straightway of those words I spoke to you in taunt and abuse." Thorstein answered that he had cared little whether he should return ever or never, but now fortune had so helped him that he was come back safe and sound.

And though they had flung out those words in some anger, they were soon well reconciled; and Thorstein now told his father all that had befallen on his journey. For this work Thorstein won good fame from everyone, as might be expected.

And soon after Thorstein had an assembly summoned, and thither came all the dwellers from the district. At this assembly Thorstein stood up and spake :

" Be this made known to you all, that the fear which has for a time lain upon us from highway robbers, so that men could not go on their journeys, is now removed and ended. This too is the chief business of my summoning your assembly, that I would have each of you take the property which has belonged to him, and to me shall belong what remains over."

Hereat the men shouted loud applause; and Thorstein won great honour for his conduct of the whole matter. The name of the evil-doer was not generally known, for it was little brought forward.

One day, Thorstein, talking with his father, said he would go east to seek earl Ingimund, as he had promised Jökull. "That were no wise counsel," said Ketill, "to put yourself in the hands of foes"; and he bade him rather stay at home. "And even should the Earl not harm you, it may well be that some will be violent and bear you no good-will."

Thorstein answered: "This I promised Jökull, and this I will perform: even though I bear back thence neither foot whole, yet thither will I go."

So Thorstein made him ready and went to Gautland: he held on his way till he came to the Earl's home early one day. The earl was out hunting, as is great men's wont. Thorstein went into a drinking-room, and sat him down on a bench with his company: then came the earl's wife into the room, and looked at those who had come, and saw that they must be strangers. She asked who they were.

Thorstein said he was a Norseman, "but I have," said he, "a private errand for yourself: go we two apart." They did so.

Then said Thorstein: "I have tidings to tell you,
even the slaying of your son Jökull."

She answered: "Great may seem such tidings, but
not unlikely, looking to his courses and evil conduct;
but what call had you to tell this tale of grief, and
travel this long way?"

Thorstein answered: "Much drew me thereto.
I promised him faithfully at our parting, that I would
go seek you and your lord, and tell the truth about
our parting: this is not to be concealed, that I
brought him to his death, because it seemed to our
countrymen impossible to sit tamely under his hand
in the matter of manslayings and plunderings. And
yet, to tell you the truth, I came into his power, and
he had the choice to kill me if he would. But he
gave me life, laying this on me withal, that I should
go seek you with his message; and you can see that
it would have been easier for me to stay at home than
to risk your mercy. Now have I here gold, which
he said you would recognise, and he bade me bear
that for a token, that you might make my peace with
the earl, with this condition, that I should receive
to wife your daughter Thordis. He also said that
he hoped you would take into account his sending
and arrangement more than my act."

Vigdis turned very red, and said, "A bold man must you be; but I think you tell the truth of your meeting with my son: and if Jökull gave you life, it would be my counsel that you should receive this, for you bear a promise of good luck in your face: and for the prayer of Jökull my son I will plead your cause with the earl, but do you be in hiding first."

And when the earl came home, his lady went to him and said: "Tidings there are to tell you, which touch us both!"

Said the earl: "You will be telling me of the death of Jökull, my son."

She said that it was so.

"He will not have died of sickness," said the earl.

She answered, "True; he was slain: and he showed before death much nobleness. He gave life to the man who wrought the deed, and sent him hither into our power with sure tokens, that you might give him pardon and remit his guilt, great though it be. Strength also might come to you from the man, if you raised him by affinity with you, giving him your daughter in marriage as Jökull proposed: who also thought you would esteem of some value his last request. And you may see how faithful this man has been to his promise, since he has travelled hither to an enemy's land from his own country, putting himself into our hands. Now I hope that for my pleading and for your own son's message you will do as I beg: look here on the tokens." She then showed him the gold.

The earl drew a deep breath wearily, and said: "You have spoken long and very boldly, urging that I should do honour to the man who has slain my son, whereas he rather deserves death than any friendly gift."

The lady said: "You have to look, my lord, on all that is in the matter: to honour the word of Jökull, and the faithfulness of the man in coming into your power; and, on another side, look to your own advanced age, needing someone to manage for you; whereto this man will be well-suited. Now, since Jökull gave him life, when he had choice of doing with him what he pleased, and this man won a lucky issue out of what seemed hopeless, our only course is not to mar that victory, to wit this man's fortune and the noble purpose of our son. A great victory, indeed, it is to contrive as Jökull has done; to give life to one who has done such offence against us; while it were the greatest shame now to do him hurt when he has trusted himself in our power."

The earl said: You support the man strongly; he
has pleased you well.   I will surely see him and judge
for myself of his worth: it will make much difference
how I like him, when my eyes see him."

Then was Thorstein led forth, and stood before
the earl; but his lady had so prepared matters, that
most of his wrath was spent.

Thorstein said: "All is in your power, sir earl, to
determine my fate: you know now on what errand
I have come hither: I offer you agreement, yet I fear
not what you may will to do.   It is, I add, the wont
of chieftains to grant life to them who of freewill
throw themselves on their grace."

The earl said: "Thou so pleasest me that I shall
grant thee life.   And this now will be the best atonement for my son, that thou take the place of a son, if
thou wilt stay with me: for the stamp of good fortune
is upon thee.   Nor is it generous to punish him who
comes freely into one's power."

Thorstein thanked the earl for the gift of life,
and he stayed there for a time; and they came to
know each other's mind.   The earl soon found that
Thorstein was a wise man, and remarkable in all
ways.

And so it was that one day Thorstein said to the

earl: "Now would I fain know, how it is to be with my marriage into your kin, my lord."

The earl answered: "I do not refuse this; it may be that this will further the fortune of our families. But this I will, that you stay with us."

Said Thorstein: "I will say yea to this, and shall feel thankful to be here during your life; but men will not grant me regard after your day: and everyone must see to his own destiny."

The earl said that that was reasonable enough.

Shortly after this Thorstein rode home, and told his father of all these plans, and asked him to go with him, which Ketill did. The earl held a feast, to which Thorstein went with Raumdalesmen and many men of rank. The feast was splendid with good viands; it ended with much honour and large gifts: and the earl and Ketill parted with great friendship. Thorstein, with his wife, remained behind. Constantly did Thorstein receive friendly messages to himself from the earl. And soon between Thorstein and Thordis there was much love.

One evening it so chanced that men came to the earl with tidings of the death of Ketill Raum, saying besides that men would have Thorstein go back to his country and rule. Thorstein put this matter before

his wife and the earl. She bade him decide, and
said she would follow his wishes. He said that his
mind was most to go home; wealth that stirred envy
he reckoned least worth; but at his home all would
best allow him honour. With this counsel the earl
agreed, saying, that at home Thorstein would have
better prospect of advancement, than among a strange
people.

Very soon after this the earl fell sick, and he called
to him Thorstein his son-in-law, and his daughter,
and spoke thus: "Now make you ready for your
journey abroad hence, that it may be with honour
and money and wealth: and our kinsmen will be well
content that all the rule in the land here be given
up to them with all thereto belonging. But, if ye
chance to have a son, let him bear my name."

Thorstein promised that it should be so; and he
said, that he coveted not the earl's title, seeing that
his own kin were untitled.

Not long after this, earl Ingimund died; but
Thorstein went home to his property and took his
father's estates. The summers he spent in warfare,
and gathered wealth and glory; in the winter he sat
at home on his estates, and was esteemed a most
honourable man.

ADVENTURE OF THORODD
SNORRI'S SON

This is from the Saga of Olaf the Holy (or St. Olaf). The battle at Stickle-stead, where Olaf fell, was fought in A.D. 1030.

THORODD SNORRI'S son (the Icelander) had been detained in Norway by king Olaf, when Gelli Thorkelsson got leave to go to Iceland. This he liked ill, that he was not free to go whither he would.

Now early in the winter, while king Olaf sat in Nidaros, he let it be known that he would send envoys to Jamtaland to gather tribute. But for this journey men were unwilling, because king Olaf's former messengers, Thrand, the White, and eleven others, had lost their lives, and the Jamtalanders had since held themselves in allegiance to the Swedish king. Then Thorodd Snorri's son offered himself for this journey: because he cared very little

what became of him, if only he could go as his own
master. The king accepted his offer, and Thorodd
went with eleven more.

They came eastward to Jamtaland, and sought the
house of one named Thorar; he was law-man there,
and in high esteem. They were received well. And
when they had been there awhile, they declared their
errand to Thorar. He said that in answering this
demand other men of the land and chiefs had no
less authority than himself; an assembly must therefore be called. This was done: the summons was
sent out, and a full assembly appointed.

Thorar went to the assembly, but the envoys remained, meanwhile, at his house. Thorar laid the
matter before the people. All were agreed that they
would pay no tribute to the king of Norway; but while
some were for hanging the messengers, others were for
reserving them as victims for sacrifice. In the end
this was decided, to keep them till the Swedish king's
stewards came: these should then dispose of them as
they would, with the consent of the people of the land.
But a show should be made of treating the messengers
well, as if they were detained to wait for the tribute:
and they were to be lodged out two and two together.
Thorodd, with one other, was at Thorar's.

At this house was held a great Yule banquet, a common ale to which each brought his share. There were many landowners in that village, and they all drank together at Yuletide. Another village was close by, wherein dwelt a brother-in-law of Thorar's, powerful and wealthy. He had a son just grown to manhood.

The brothers-in-law were to drink half the Yule at either's house, and first at Thorar's. The brothers-in-law drank together, and Thorodd drank with the son of Thorar's brother-in-law. And there were drinking-matches, and in the evening talking-matches, and comparisons of Norsemen and Swedes, and then of their kings both former and present, and further of the dealings that had been between the two countries in manslayings and raids. And here the goodman's son said: "If our kings have lost more men, the royal stewards will soon balance that with the lives of twelve men, when they come from the south after Yule. You little know, wretched men, for what you are being reserved." This set Thorodd a-thinking. Many grinned at him and his comrade, and aimed mocking words at them and their king. And, as the ale spoke in the Jamtalanders, that secret was now out, which Thorodd had not before suspected.

Next day Thorodd and his companion took all
their clothing and weapons, and put them ready to
hand; and the following night, when men slept, they
ran away to the wood.   But on the morrow, their
flight being discovered, men pursued them with slot-
hounds, and found them in the wood where they had
hidden themselves; and they brought them back, and
put them in a separate building, wherein was a deep
vault, into which they were lowered, and a door was
set thereover.   They had little food, and no clothes
save what they stood in.

When Mid-Yule came, Thorar and all the freed-
men with him went to his brother-in-law's; he was
there to drink the other half of the Yule feast.
Thorar's thralls were left in charge of the vault.   But
plenty of drink was allowed them, and this they did
not spare, so that very soon in the evening they
became ale-mad.   And when they had drunk their
fill, then those who were to take food to the men in
the vault said amongst themselves that there should
be no stint.   Thorodd sang songs and amused the
thralls; they said he was a capital fellow, and
gave him a very large candle lighted.   Then those
thralls who were first within the building, came
out and called eagerly to the others that they should

go in. And each of the two sets were ale-mad, so that they did not shut behind them either vault or building.

Then Thorodd and his comrade tore their cloaks into strips and knit them together, and rolled up one end into a ball, and threw it up to the floor of the room above. It wound itself round the foot of a chest and was fast. Then they tried to go up, and Thorodd lifted his comrade till he stood on his shoulders: he then hauled himself up through the opening. In the room there was no lack of rope, and he lowered rope down to Thorodd. But when he had to pull Thorodd up, he could not manage it. Then Thorodd told him to cast the rope over the cross-beam that was in the building, and to make a loop at the end, and put in it wood and stone, more than would balance his weight. He did so: whereupon this sank down into the vault, and Thorodd came up.

They took to them clothes that were in the room, such as they needed. There were some reindeer skins there; of these they cut off the feet and bound them on their own feet heel foremost. But before they went away they set fire to a large corn-barn there, and then ran away in the mirk of a moonless

night. The corn-barn was burned, as were many
other houses in the village.

Thorodd and his comrade went all that night
through the wild, and hid themselves by day. In the
morning they were missed, and slot-hounds were set
to track them every way from the building. But the
hounds followed the trail back to the building, because
they smelt the reindeer's feet and followed as their
hoofmarks pointed : thus the men could not be found.

Long did Thorodd and his comrade travel through
the wild, till they came one evening to a little house,
and went in. There sat by the fire a man and a
woman : the man named himself Thorir, and said
that she who sat there was his wife, and the cottage
was theirs. The goodman offered them shelter there:
this was accepted. He said that he had fled from
men's abodes thither by reason of a manslaughter.

Kind hospitality was shown to Thorodd and his
companion : they all ate their meal together by the
fire. Then for the guests a bed was strown on the
bench, and they lay down to sleep. There was still
some glow in the fire. Thorodd's companion slept,
but Thorodd being yet awake, saw a man come out of
another room. Never had he seen so big a man.
He wore scarlet clothes laced with gold, and was

splendid in appearance. Thorodd heard him blame the pair for taking in guests, when they had barely food for themselves. The housewife answered: "Be not angry, brother; 'tis but once in a way. Rather thyself give them some help; thou art better able to do so than we." Thorodd heard the big man called Arnljot Gellini; also that the housewife was his sister. Of Arnljot he had heard before, and knew this of him, that he was a noted robber and evil-doer.

Thorodd and the other slept that night, for they were weary with travel. But when about a third of the night remained, Arnljot came to them and bade them rise and make ready for their way. At once they rose and dressed; breakfast was given them. Then Thorir brought snowshoes for them both. Arnljot made him ready to go with them; he mounted his snowshoes, which were both broad and long. But at the first stroke of his staff he shot far ahead. Then he waited, and said that they would never get on at that rate; so he bade them mount his snowshoes. They did so, Thorodd going close to him and holding on under Arnljot's belt, while his comrade held on to him. Arnljot then slid on as fast as if he were going free.

Late in the following night they came to a house of

refuge, where they made them a fire and prepared a meal.
But, as they were eating, Arnljot spake and bade them
throw down nothing of their meat, neither bones nor
crumbs.   He took out of his shirt a silver dish and
ate off it.   When they were filled, Arnljot gathered up
the remains.   They then made them ready for bed.   In
one end of the house was a loft resting upon a cross-
tree: into this they and Arnljot climbed, and lay
down to sleep.   Arnljot had a large halberd, the
socket whereof was overlaid with gold, and the shaft
stood so high that the hand could well grasp the
socket, and he was girded with a sword.   The other
two had their weapons and clothes up in the loft by
them.   Arnljot bade them be silent; he lay outer-
most in the loft.

A little later twelve men came in: chapmen they
were, travelling to Jamtaland with their wares.   But
when they came into the house, they made a great
noise and were merry, and kindled them large fires:
and when they ate they threw away all the bones.
Then they made them ready for bed, and lay down
on the bench by the fire.

When they had slept a little while, there entered
the house a big troll-wife, and coming in she swept
up from around her in a trice bones and all that was

eatable, and crammed it into her mouth, then seized the man nearest to her, tore and rent him to bits, and cast him on the fire. Then the others waked as with an evil dream, and leapt up. These she did to death one after the other, till but one remained alive. He ran in under the loft, and called for help, if any were there in the loft that could save him. Arnljot stretched down towards him, took him by the shoulders, and snatched him up into the loft. Then the troll-wife turned her to the fire, and began to eat the men who were roasted: but Arnljot stood up, and grasping his halberd, thrust it between her shoulders, so that the point came out at the breast. She started, uttered a hideous cry, and dashed out. The spear was forced from Arnljot's hand, she carried it away with her.

Arnljot went and cleared away the dead, and set up again the door before the room, for she had broken it all down as she went out. They then slept for what remained of the night.

At dawn of day they rose, and first they ate their breakfast: but when they had eaten, then said Arnljot: "Now we will part here: you must go back by this road, by which the chapmen came hither yesterday; but I will go and seek my spear. I shall

take for my wages, whatever I think useful of the
goods that belonged to these men. And thou,
Thorodd, shalt bear to king Olaf my greeting, and
tell him that he is the one man whom I most desire
to meet, though he will think my greeting nothing
worth." He took up the silver dish, and wiped it
with a cloth, and said : "Take to the king this dish,
say that this is my greeting."

Then both he and they made them ready for their
travel, and so they parted. Thorodd and his comrade
went their way, and with them that one of the chapmen who had escaped. Thorodd went till he found
king Olaf in the town of Nidaros ; and he told him
all about his journey, and gave him Arnljot's greeting
and the silver dish.

The king said that 'twas ill-done that Arnljot had
not come to meet him ; "a great pity it is, that so
brave a fellow should be concerned in such wrong-
doings."

Thorodd remained with the king for the rest of the
winter : the next summer he got leave to go to Iceland. He and king Olaf parted friends.

Of Arnljot there is yet this to be told. Shortly
before the battle in which king Olaf fell, while the
king was at Sticklestead, a man came to him like to no

other man, for he was so tall, that none there reached more than to his shoulders. Handsome he was to look upon, and fair-haired. He was well armed, had a beautiful helmet and a coat of ring-mail, was girded with a sword, and in his hand he bare a large spear, overlaid with gold, whose shaft was so thick as to fill the hand. This man came before the king, greeted him, and asked if the king would accept his service. The king asked him of his name and kin, and from what land he was.

He answered: "I have kin in Jamtaland and Helsingjaland: I am named Arnljot Gellini; this chiefly I may tell thee besides, that I lent help to thy men whom thou sentest to Jamtaland to gather tribute. I gave into their hands a silver dish, which I sent to thee as a token that I would fain be thy friend."

Then the king asked whether he were a Christian or no.

He said this of his faith, that he believed in his own might and main: "this faith," said he, "hath sufficed me hitherto: but now I purpose rather to believe in thee, O king."

The king answered: "If thou wilt believe in me, thou must believe that which I teach thee. This

must thou believe, that Jesus Christ created heaven
and earth, and all men, and to him shall go after
death all those who are good and right-believing."

Arnljot answered: "I have heard tell of a White
Christ, but I know nought of his doings, or where he
bears rule.   But now I will believe all thou tellest
me : all my counsel I will trust in thy hand."   After
this Arnljot was baptized, the king teaching him such
part of the faith as he deemed most needful.

And he set him in a place in the van of the host,
before the standard.   There also were Gauka Thorir
and Afrafasti and their following ; and with these, in
the first bout of the battle, Arnljot fell.

FROM THE STORY OF SIGURD
JORSALAFARA

The two brothers Eystein and Sigurd succeeded Magnus Bare-legs in 1103. Sigurd's expedition to Jerusalem was in 1107—1111. Sigurd died 1130.

HAROLD GILLI AND MAGNUS

IN the reign of Sigurd, son of Magnus Barelegs, Halkell Huk, baron in Mœra, sailed west over sea to the southern isles. Thither came out to him from Ireland a man named Gilli-Christ, who said he was a son of Magnus Barelegs: his mother accompanied him, and said that he had another name, Harold.

Halkell received this man, and conveyed him to Norway, and at once went to king Sigurd with Harold and his mother. They two declared their errand before the king; and king Sigurd discussed the matter with his chiefs. Some spoke one way, some another; all bade the king decide it, but the

more part were against Harold's claim; and the king
was the more set on his own will.

He then had Harold summoned to him, and said
he would not refuse him the right to prove his parentage by ordeal, while he would have this secured, that,
even though his parentage were established to be as
he asserted, he should not claim the kingdom during
the lives of himself, Sigurd, and his son Magnus; and
this agreement was confirmed with oaths. King
Sigurd said that Harold should tread hot iron bars in
proof of his parentage, which ordeal was thought
to be rather harsh, seeing that he was, by the
ordeal, to prove his parentage, but not to win the
kingdom.

However, Harold consented to this, and fasted for
the ordeal by iron; and this was the greatest ordeal
ever known in Norway: nine red-hot ploughshares
were laid down, and Harold walked over them bare-
foot, led by two bishops, and calling the while on
St. Columba. His bed was ready on the spot.

Then said Magnus, king Sigurd's son: "He treads
not the iron boldly."

The king answered: "Thou speakest ill and sav-
agely: he hath borne him in manly wise."

At the end Harold let himself fall on the bed; and

after three days, when the issue of the ordeal was tested, his feet were found unburnt.

After that king Sigurd acknowledged the kinship of Harold; but Magnus his son disliked him much, and many chiefs inclined to Magnus. King Sigurd trusted so fully his own popularity with all in the land, that he requested all men to swear that Magnus his son should alone be king after him, and he took oaths to this effect of all the people of the land.

Harold Gilli was a tall man, slender of build, long-necked, rather long-faced, black-eyed, dark-haired, alert and quick; very Irish in dress, wearing short and light clothing. Harold had great difficulty with the Norse tongue, and stammered much for words: and many men made a mock of this, but king Sigurd would not let this pass when he was by.

It was usual that Harold should attend the king to his sleeping-room of an evening, but once it so chanced that those about Magnus got him to stay behind, and they sat long and drank. Harold was talking with another man: and speaking of Ireland, he said that there were men in Ireland so fleet of foot that no horse could outstrip them in a race.

Magnus, the king's son, heard this, and said: "Now he again lies, as is his wont."

Harold answered: "It is truth that men can be found in Ireland whom no horse in Norway can gallop past." About this they had some words; both had drunk deeply.

Magnus had had sent to him a horse from Gotland, a perfect treasure, very fast. About this they who were present spoke, saying that there was no horse so fast; and they turned towards Harold. Then said Magnus: "Here shalt thou wager thine head, that thou canst run as fast as I can ride my horse; and I will lay against it my gold ring."

Said Harold: "I did not say that I would run so fast, but that I could find men out in Ireland who could run so fast; and on that I will wager."

Magnus answered: "I shall not go to Ireland; we two must wager here, not there."

Harold then went away to bed, and would have no more to do with him. This happened at Oslo.

But next morning, when matins were ended, Magnus, riding his fast Gotland horse, went up to the road, and sent word to Harold to come thither. When Harold came, he was thus drest: he wore a shirt, and breeks strapped under his soles, a short mantle, an Irish cap on his head, a spearshaft in his hand.

Magnus was marking the course. Harold said: "Thou art making it too long." Magnus at once made it much longer, and said, it was even so too short. Many men were present.

Then they raced over the course forwards, and Harold kept ever level with the horse's shoulders: but when they came to the end, Magnus said; "Thou heldest on by the girth-strap, and the horse drew thee." They had another race back; and now Harold ran all the course just before the horse; and when they came to the end, Harold asked: "Did I then hold on by the girth-strap?"

Magnus answered: "Thou heldest by the bridle."

Then Magnus let his horse breathe awhile ; but when he was ready, he set spurs to the horse, who quickly got into his gallop. Harold stood still. Then Magnus looked back, and called out "Run now." Then Harold bounded off, and soon passed the horse and went far ahead, and kept so to the end of the course. He came in so far in front that he lay down, and then sprang up and greeted his kinsman Magnus when he came there. After that they went home to the house.

But king Sigurd had been at high mass the while, and knew nought of this till after the mid-day meal.

Then he said angrily to Magnus: "Thou callest Harold home-bred and silly. Methinks thou art the greater fool: thou art ignorant of men's manners in foreign lands: thou knowest not that men of foreign lands train themselves to other accomplishments rather than to guzzle ale and make themselves mad and helpless and lost to all sense of what befits a man. Give thou to Harold the ring he hath won: and never henceforth jeer at him, while my head is above ground and I am master."

KING SIGURD AND OTTAR BRIGHTING

IT is told that king Sigurd was at a certain banquet in Upland, and there baths were prepared; but when the king was in the bath, the tub being tented over, it seemed as though a fish darted close past him in the tub. Then he was seized with such a fit of laughter that it brought on a restlessness and madness; and afterwards such attacks very often came upon him.

No more noble character ('tis said by all) nor wiser ruler has there been in Norway than king Sigurd, and he was deemed a chief of great mark and glorious by reason of his journey to the east. But, as time wore on, he was hardly able to control his mood and temper from breaking out, now and then, in acts of wrong and outrage.

The story goes that once, on the feast of Whit-Sunday, king Sigurd sate at table with a large company and many of his friends; and when he came to his high seat, men saw that he sate with great weakness and had a heavy countenance. They feared for him how it might end.

The king gazed at the people, raising his eyes and glaring around him at those on the dais; but none of his men dared to speak to him. He then took up a costly book which he had brought into the land: it was written all with letters of gold, so that no greater treasure in the way of a book had ever come into Norway. His queen was sitting there by him.

Then spake king Sigurd: "Much can change," said he, "in a man's life. I had two things that I thought the best, when I came into the land: they were this book and the queen. But now I think each worse and more hateful than the other: of all that I now possess methinks they are the worst. The queen does not perceive how hideous she is, with a goat's-horn standing out of her head; and the better she seemed to me once, the worse she seems to me now. And this book is good for nothing!" With that he cast away the book on the fire that was burning on the hall floor; but he smote the queen a blow on the cheek close to the eye. The queen wept, yet more for the malady of the king than for the blow or offence done to herself.

There was one standing before the king, whose name was Ottar Brighting, a yeoman's son, a link-boy of the king's, who was on service there for the day. He was small of stature, graceful, valiant, bold, and pleasant; dark of hair and skin, so that it seemed a jesting nickname to call him Brighting.

He bounded over and snatched out of the fire the book which the king had thrown there, and holding it he thus addressed the king: "Unlike days were those, sire, when thou sailedst with pomp and pride back to Norway, and camest into this land with great fame and glory: wherefore then all thy friends ran to meet thee with joy and welcomed thy coming, and all consented to thee as king, and would have thee over them with much honour and renown: but now are come over us days of mourning. For on this chief feast-day hither are come to thee many of thy friends, who cannot be cheerful by reason of thy gloom and weakness. It were to be wished that thou couldst be glad with them. Now may it please thee, good my lord, accept this wholesome counsel: and first be reconciled with the queen, and gladden her with kindness, whom thou hast treated with much wrong; and thereafter do the like to all thy friends and liegemen: this is my counsel."

Then said king Sigurd: "Wilt thou give me counsel, a wretched cottar's son, a silly farmer-lad of the lowest kin, and sprung from base and beggarly stock?" And he leapt up, and raised his sword, brandishing it at Ottar with both hands, and made as if he would cut him down.

But Ottar stood motionless and upright, nor stirred from his place, nor started, nor blenched, as being utterly fearless; and the king turned the sword so that the blade came down flat towards Ottar's head, and then swerving outwards, smote softly on his shoulder.

Then was he silent, and sate him down in the high seat. Silent too were all men that were in the hall, none daring to address a word to him. Soon the king looked round more gently than before, and then he spoke.

"It takes long to try men, of what manner they be. There sate my friends, barons, marshals, pages, all the best of the land; and not one bore him so well to-ward me as did this man, whom ye may think little worth compared to yourselves, but now he loved me most. I came here a madman, and wished to destroy my treasure: he saved this, not fearing death. He then spoke his errand fair, tempering his words to do me honour; while he said nothing whereby my malady would be increased; from all such things he refrained, though with truth he might have spoken them: but so noble was his speech, that the wisest here could not have spoken more eloquently. And then I leapt up frantic, and made as if I would cut him down; but he was undaunted, as if there were nought to fear; and, when I saw that, I let this work pass undone, undeserving as he was of hurt.

Now shall ye my friends know how I will reward him. Hitherto he hath been link-boy, now shall he be my baron; and this shall follow, which will not be less, that he shall henceforth be of chief mark among my barons."

Then the king thanked the yeoman's son in the presence of them all, for that he had calmed his evil mood with wise words and bold heart, and had done that which none of his great barons dared. And he made him his highest baron.

King Sigurd was often taken by these passionate fits and strange ways: and whoso of his poor servants would then admonish him, to them he listened best, and gave them goods and houses for such service.

Ottar became, afterwards, a man of renown in Norway, for many good and glorious deeds.

A GAME AT COMPARISONS
BETWEEN TWO BROTHER KINGS

WHILE Sigurd was absent abroad, Eystein his
brother had done many useful works in the
land. He had in many ways bettered the condition
of the people in his country, upholding well the laws.

Eystein was a man of very comely countenance,
blue-eyed and somewhat open-eyed, his hair was
flaxen-white and curly; he was not tall, but of middle
height: prudent in wit he was, learned in all laws,
customs, and histories; ready with counsel, wise in
words, and eloquent, liberal of money; very cheerful
and courteous, liked and loved by all.

Sigurd was a tall man, and a strong, brown-haired,
of noble mien, not comely of countenance, but well-
proportioned: a man whose words were very few,
nor always kind, but a good friend and staunch: no
great talker; in morals, good and honourable. King

Sigurd was a born commander, severe in discipline, himself keeping to the law; liberal of money, a powerful and excellent king.

King Eystein and king Sigurd went both one winter to banquets in Upland, where each of them had a residence. But as these residences were not far apart, it was settled that they should be entertained together in turn at the house of either. They were first together at the house belonging to Eystein.

In the evening, when men began to drink, the beer was not good, and men were sad.

Then said king Eystein: "Men are sad, tho' 'tis custom at an ale that men be merry: find we some pastime over our ale; so will men be stirred to mirth. Brother Sigurd, all will think it seemliest that we too begin some amusing talk."

King Sigurd answered rather peevishly: "Be thou as talkative as thou wilt; but pray give me leave to be silent."

King Eystein said: "This has often been a custom at an ale, that men choose rival heroes. I will have it so here."

King Sigurd sat silent.

"I see," said Eystein, "that I shall have to begin this pastime. I will take thee, brother, to compare

with myself.   And this I lay down, that we are both
equal as to name, equal as to possessions; nor do
I make any difference between us in birth and up-
bringing."

Then answered king Sigurd: "Dost thou not
remember that I could force thee backward when I
wished, tho' thou wast a year older?"

King Eystein answered: "I remember this no
less, that thou didst not take to such sport as needed
agility."

Then said king Sigurd: "Rememberest thou how
it went with us in swimming?   I could put thee
under water whenever I would."

Eystein said: "I swam no shorter distance than
thou, and was not a worse sea-swimmer.   Skill have
I, too, on ice-skates, so that I know no man who
could match me: but thou hast no more skill that
way than an ox."

King Sigurd answered: "A more princely and
useful accomplishment, I deem it, to be skilled with
the bow: thou, I believe, couldst not bend my bow,
tho' thou shouldst set thy foot against it."

Eystein said: "I am not so bow-strong as thou
art; but for straight shooting there is little odds
between us.   And I have far better skill than thou

hast on snowshoes; and that has ever been held a good accomplishment."

Sigurd said: "'Tis thought to be a princely distinction that he who is to be ruler over other men should be tall above his troop, strong, and better at his weapons than others, easily seen, easily known, when many are together."

Eystein said: "No less is this a distinguishing mark, that a man be comely: for on comeliness brave apparel sits well. I am also much more learned in law than thou; and whatever we may talk about, I am much more fluent."

Sigurd answered: "It may be thou hast learned more tricks of law, for I had other work to do. And I question not thy fluency of speech. But many say that thou are not very true to thy word, and that it matters little what thou dost promise; thou speakest to suit those who at the time are present. And this is not kingly."

Eystein answered: "It happens thus, when men bring their causes before me; I first think to end each man's cause as he would best like: then comes often another who pleads against the first; whereupon the matter is so balanced and compromised as to content both. Moreover I promise, when I am asked, because I would that all men should go gladdened from my presence. I see that there is the choice open to do as thou dost, to promise ill to all. But I do not hear my performance of promises challenged."

Sigurd answered: "It has been the public talk, that the travel which I travelled abroad was very princely: but thou satest at home like thy father's daughter."

Eystein answered: "Now art thou touching the very sore. I would not have waked this debate, had I known no answer here. To me it seemed almost this, that I had to send thee from home, as it had been my sister, before thou wert ready for the journey."

Sigurd answered: "Thou wilt have heard that I had many battles in Saracenland, and won victory in all; and many treasures won I, the like of which have never come into this country. There was I thought most worth, where I found the noblest men; but I believe that thou hast not yet rid thee of home-sloth. I travelled to Jerusalem, and I came by South Italy, and I saw thee not there, brother. In Sicily I gave the title of king to the great earl Roger. I won eight battles, and thou wert at none of them.

I went to the Sepulchre of the Lord, and I saw thee not there, brother. I went to the river Jordan, in which the Lord was baptized, and swam out over the river, and I saw thee not there. But on the bank was a brushwood copse, and I knit for thee a knot there in the copse, and it awaits thee there; and I declared that thou must loose it, brother, or else bear such conditions as were then laid upon thee."

King Eystein then said: "A small set-off shall I have against all this. Northwards in Mœra I established fishermen's booths, where poor starving men might get food; and I gave maintenance for a priest there, and paid down money for the church, where almost all before was heathen. Men there will remember that Eystein has been king in Norway. Over the Dovrefell lay the route from Throndheim; men were constantly out there, and many made that toilsome journey. I caused a hospice to be built, and gave money for it: men will know there too that Eystein has been king in Norway. By Agdaness the coast was wild and harbourless, many ships passed that way; there now is a harbour, and good anchorage, and a church. Afterwards, I caused beacons to be set upon the high fells: of this, all men in the land will now get the benefit. I had built the royal hall

in Bjorgyn, and the Apostle's church, and the
staircase between: the kings who come after will
remember my name there. Michael's church I had
built, and the monastery. Laws also I established,
brother, that each might have right of his fellow:
and, if these be kept, the government will go on
better. I had the steeple built in Sinholmssound
with iron rings. The people of Jamtaland we
brought under our rule, more by gentle words than
by force and war. Now these are small things to
reckon: yet am I not sure that for the dwellers in
the country they are less useful than thy doings, tho'
thou didst chop up blackmen as foes in Saracen land,
and so hurl them to hell-doom. And whereas thou
vauntest thy good works, I think it may serve my
soul's health no less that I established the holy friars.
And as to the knot thou tiedst for me out there, I
shall never loose it: but I might have tied thee a
knot, had I so willed, that would have taken thee
longer to loose, at the time when thou returning
home sailedst with one ship into my fleet. Let wise
men now look to it, what thou hast that is more
excellent than mine. And know this, ye gold-
necks, that men in Norway may yet compare with
you."

After that the kings were silent, and each of the twain was wroth. More things there were in the dealings between these brothers, in which each put forward himself and his cause, and would fain be greater than the other. Yet peace held between them while they lived.

VERSE TRANSLATIONS

FROM THE OLDER EDDA

BALDER'S DREAMS

OR

WAYFARER'S LAY

THE Balder legend is one of the best known of the Scandinavian mythology : how he dreamed boding dreams, how he was secured from hurt by an oath taken from all things save one mistletoe branch, how by this in blind Hodœr's hand he fell slain. Then Hel agreed to let him go back, if all things should weep him. All things were bidden to do so; but one hag refused, saying, "Let Hel keep her own."

This *Wayfarer's Lay* tells of Odin's descent to learn about Balder's danger. Our own poet Gray has written an ode on this, "The Descent of Odin." Matthew Arnold has written a poem "Balder dead." Both these are beautiful ; unlike each other, and, we may say, unlike their simple rugged originals. The prose original of the whole legend is in Snorri's Edda : the poetical Edda gives *Vegtams Kvida*. I have followed Möbius's text, and have endeavoured, while keeping close to the Icelandic, to preserve something of the alliterations, accents, and length of the lines.

1

SOON were all gods
In council gathered,
And goddesses all
To grave debate :
And hereon pondered
The powers divine,
Wherefore dreamed Balder
The dreams of bale.

2

Uprose Odin,
Ancient sire,
And on Swift-glider
Saddle he laid :
Down rode he then
To darksome Hell,
And met the hound
That from Hell forth-came.

3

Bloody before him
Reeked that hound's breast,
At the Father of spells
Full long he bayed :

Onward rode Odin,
Earth 'neath him groaned,
Till to the high hold
Of Hell he came.

4

Then rode Odin
To the Eastern gate,
Where he knew that the seeress
Sepulchred lay.
To that witchwife he spake
Corse-wakening spells,
Till unwilling uprose she,
A voice of the dead.

5

" What man is this
To me unknown,
Who loads with more trouble
My toil-worn soul ?
By snow snowed over,
By rains sore-smit,
By dew-drift drenchèd,
Long dead have I lain."

6

Odin.   " Wayfarer hight I,
         Warfarer's son :
         Thou'll teach me of Hell,
         I tell thee of Earth.
         For whom are the benches
         With bright rings bestrown,
         And the festal rooms
         Made fair with gold ? "

7

Seeress.   " Here stands for Balder,
           New-brewed mead,
           Sheer drink in bowls
           With shield o'erlidded ;
           And gods' sons here wait
           Gleeful their guest.
           Need-driven I spake,
           Now silent will be."

8

Odin.   " Seeress, no silence !
         I seek yet more,
         Till all I learn ;
         Thy lore I yet ask :

Who shall to Balder
Be cause of bane,
And Odin's son
Of life bereave?"

9

Seeress.   " Hoder shall bear
The high branch renowned ;
He shall to Balder
Be cause of bane,
And Odin's son
Of life bereave.
Need-driven, I spake,
Now silent will be."

10

Odin.   " Seeress, no silence !
I seek yet more,
Till all I learn ;
Thy lore I yet ask :
Who will on Hoder
Wage vengeful feud,
And Balder's bane
To the death-pyre bring ?"

11

Seeress.   " Rindr in western halls
Rears to Odin a son ;
He weapons shall wield
When one night old :
Nor hand shall he wash,
Nor head shall he comb,
Till Balder's bane
To death-pyre he bring.

12

Need-driven, I spake,
Now silent will be."
Odin.   " Seeress, no silence !
I seek yet more.
Who be the maidens
That moaning weep,
And cast up heavenwards
Their neck-veiling hoods ? "

13

Seeress.   " No wayfarer thou,
As I weened erewhile :
Thou'rt rather Odin,
Ancient sire."

Odin.   " No Seeress thou,
            Nor witchwife wise;
            Thou'rt rather the mother
            Of giants three."

14

Seeress. " Ride thou home, Odin,
            Reap boast herefrom.
            None thus again cometh
            My news to know,
            Till Loki from bonds
            Shall loosened pass,
            Till direful bursteth
            The high gods' doom."

FROM THE YOUNGER EDDA

THE MILL SONG

THIS curious poem, *Grotta-songr*, rendered variously "Grit-song" or "Grinding Song," is attached in the prose "Edda" to the Story of Frodi's Mill. A painstaking German translator, Volzogen, thinks it a "year-myth." As to the details he does not convince me. Grain, the oldest wealth of the earth, may be partly the foundation of the myth about a wealth-grinding mill. Excessive greed of wealth works ruin. Also perhaps there lurks the lesson that, while the forces of nature are useful servants, they may, if over-strained, work destruction.

Besides being in the younger "Edda," this lay is also in Sæmund's "Edda."

I

NOW are they come
   To the king's house,
Fenja and Menja,
Fore-knowing pair.
They bide with Frodi
Fridleif's son,
Mighty maidens
As menials held.

2

The twain to the flour-bin,
Forthwith were led;
They bade the grey granite
A-grinding run.
No rest king Frodi
Nor respite gave;
At once would he hear
His handmaids' sound.

3

They croon'd to the mill-wheel's
Deep-murmuring hum,
They sang as they swang
The swift-spinning stone;
Till servants of Frodi
All slumbering lay:
Then thus spake Menja,
Who stood at the mill:

4

" Wealth grind we for Frodi,
Grind we pure bliss,
Full measure of money
In mill of joy:

On wealth be his sitting,
On down be his sleeping,
To gladness his waking:
Such grist were well ground.

5

Hurt to his fellow
Here none shall frame;
Bale none shall bring,
Bane none shall work;
None shall smite vengeful
With sword's keen blade,
Tho' his brother's slayer
Bound he should meet.

6

Now leave we the flour-bin,
Let the stone stand."
But the master still bade
The maids grind on:
" Sleep ye no more
Than sleeps the house-crower;
Stay ye no longer
Than one stave I sing.

7

Thou wast not, Frodi,
Thou friend of men,
Foresighted in bargain,
Thy bondwomen buying.
Thou chosest by strength,
By stature to look on,
Of kith and kin
Nought caring to ask.

8

Rough wight was Hrungnir,
Rough was his sire,
Yet these did Thiassi
In thews surpass :
Idi and Orni
Our forefathers were,
Hill-giants' brethren ;
Hence were we born.

9

Ne'er had come Grotti
From gray fell-side,
That boulder hard
From bosom of earth :

Nor thus would grind
Grim giant maid,
Had men but wotted,
Whence she claim'd kin.

10

Playmates we twain
For winters nine
Were nourished to strength
In nethermost earth.
We wrought as maidens
In mighty works,
Rocky ridges
We rent from their base.

11

To giants' stronghold
Stones we upheaved,
While shook beneath them
The shivering ground.
We slang up in such wise
The spinning boulders,
That men might reach them,
Those massy crags.

12

Soon thereafter
In Sweden's realm
Foreseers twain
The fray we sought.
Brute bears we hunted,
We brake war-shields;
Charged mightily through
Gray mail-clad throng:

13

O'erthrew one monarch,
Upbore another;
To gallant Gothorm
Gave we our aid,
Nor sate men quiet,
Till Knui fell.

14

For seasons many
So held we on,
In warlike combats
Winning renown:

There did we shear
With sharp lance-point,
Till wounds were bloody,
And sword-blades red.

15

Now are we come
To a king's high house;
Here bide we unpitied
As bond-slaves held.
Clay gnaws our footsoles,
Cold stings our heads;
Frodi's war-queller
We wearily turn.

16

Let hands have respite,
Let stone be still!
Myself large measure
Of mill-work have wrought.
Nay, but our labour
No lightening finds,
Till Frodi our grinding
Fulfill'd shall deem.

17

Lo hands of heroes
Holding hard pikes,
Weapons blood-dripping :
Wake, Frodi, wake !
Wake, Frodi, wake,
If thou wouldst hearken
To the songs we sing,
To the saws of old.

18

Fire see I blazing
East from the burgh ;
From watchmen's beacon
Is war-news, I wot.
In hot haste hither
A host will come,
And the proud palace
Of prince will burn.

19

The throne of Hleidr
Thou, Frodi, shalt lose,
The rings of the red gold,
The rocks divine.

Swiftlier whirl we,
Sister, the mill ;
Not yet are we whelm'd,
War-maiden, in gore.

20

My father's daughter
Hath forcefully ground ;
For warriors full many
' Fey ' hath she seen.
The flour-bin's strong staves
Starting all break
With iron girding ;
Yet grind we on !

21

Yet grind we on !
By grandson of Halfdan,
By son of Yrsa
Falls Frodi slain.
Her son, her brother,
Both is he call'd ;
The two-fold kinship
We twain best know."

22

With might and with main
The maidens ground,
In giant fury
Fierce and young.
The shaft-wood shiver'd,
Fell shatter'd the bin,
The mill-stone boulder
Burst all in twain.

23

This word then spake she
That giant bride:
" Of grist our venture,
O Frodi, is ground.
Long time at the mill
Have the maidens stood."

FROM EGIL'S SAGA

HEAD-RANSOM

THE circumstances of this poem may be read in the Egilssaga, chapters 62, 63. Egil, shipwrecked on the north-east coast of England, went boldly before king Eric, his bitter enemy, who was then in York, being governor of Northumberland for king Athelstan. Condemned to death, Egil, by the advice of his friend Arinbjorn, composed and recited a poem in Eric's praise, and received for it his life.

I

WESTWARD I sailed the wave,
    Within me Odin gave
The sea of song I bear
(So 'tis my wont to fare):
I launched my floating oak
When loosening ice-floes broke,
My mind a galleon fraught
With load of minstrel thought.

2

A prince doth hold me guest,
Praise be his due confess'd :
Of Odin's mead let draught
In England now be quaff'd.
Laud bear I to the king,
Loudly his honour sing ;
Silence I crave around,
My song of praise is found.

3

Sire, mark the tale I tell,
Such heed beseems thee well :
Better I chaunt my strain,
If stillness hush'd I gain.
The monarch's wars in word
Widely have peoples heard,
But Odin saw alone
Bodies before him strown.

4

Swell'd of swords the sound
Smiting bucklers round,
Fiercely waxed the fray,
Forward the king made way.

Streamed red glaives in gore,
Stunned were ears with roar,
Iron hailstorm's song,
Heavy, loud and long.

5
Lances, a woven fence,
Well-ordered bristle dense;
On royal ships in line
Exulting spearmen shine.
Soon dark with bloody stain
Seethed there an angry main,
With war-fleet's thundering sound,
With wounds and din around.

6
Of men many a rank
Mid showering darts sank:
Glory and fame
Gat Eric's name.

7
More may yet be told.
An men silence hold:

Further feats and glory,
Fame hath noised in story.
Warriors' wounds were rife,
Where the chief waged strife ;
Shivered swords with stroke
On blue shield-rims broke.

8

Breast-plates ringing crashed,
Burning helm-fire flashed,
Biting point of glaive
Bloody wound did grave.
Baldric's crystal blade
Bowed and prostrate laid
Odin's oaks (they say)
In that iron-play.

9

Spears crossing dashed,
Sword-edges clashed :
Glory and fame
Gat Eric's name.

10

Red blade the king did wield,
Ravens flocked o'er the field.
Dripping spears flew madly,
Darts with aim full deadly.
Scotland's scourge let feed
Wolf, the Ogress' steed:
Eagles full and fain
Feasted on the slain.

11

Soared battle-cranes
O'er corse-strown lanes,
Found flesh-fowl's bill
Of blood its fill.
While deep the wound
He delves, around
Grim raven's beak
Blood-fountains break.

12

Axe furnished feast
For Ogress' beast:
Eric on the wave
To wolves flesh-banquet gave.

13

Javelins flying sped,
Peace affrighted fled :
Bows were bent amain,
Wolves were battle-fain :
Spears in shivers split,
Sword-teeth keenly bit ;
Archers' strings loud sang,
Arrows forward sprang.

14

He back his buckler flings
From arm beset with rings,
Swordplay-stirrer good,
Spiller of foemen's blood.
Waxing everywhere
(Witness true I bear),
East o'er billows came
Eric's sounding name.

15

Bent the king his yew,
Bees wound-bearing flew :
Eric on the wave
To wolves flesh-banquet gave.

16

I to men were fain
Yet to make more plain
High-soul'd mood of king,
But must swiftly sing.
Weapons when he takes,
The battle-goddess wakes,
On ships' shielded side
Streams the battle-tide.

17

Gems from wrist he gives,
Glittering armlets rives:
Lavish ring-despiser
Loves not hoarding miser.
Frodi's flour of gold
Gladdens rovers bold;
Prince bestoweth scorning
Pebbles hand-adorning.

18

Foemen might not stand
For his deathful brand;
Yew-bow loudly sang,
Sword-blades meeting rang,

Lances aye were cast,
Still he the land held fast,
Proud Eric prince renowned;
And praise his feats hath crowned.

19

Monarch, at thy will
Judge my minstrel skill:
Silence thus to find
Sweetly cheered my mind.
Moved my mouth with word
From my heart's ground stirred,
Draught of Odin's wave
Due to warrior brave.

20

Silence I have broken,
A sovereign's glory spoken:
Words I knew well-fitting
Warrior-council sitting.
Praise from heart I bring,
Praise to honoured king:
Plain I sang and clear,
Song that all could hear.

SONS' LOSS

BODVAR, Eric's favourite son, was drowned by misadventure
(Egilss. chapter 71). The father, at first inconsolable, resolved
to starve himself. But his daughter persuades him to live and
compose this poem. It is the most remarkable of Egil's poems :
it is not like most Icelandic poems ; it is of deep pathos. "How
can I live (sings the poet) after such losses? Father, mother,
brother gone ! First one son, then another. The world holds
no comfort for me. No vengeance is possible on the powers or
sea and storm. Odin, god of battles, helps me not ; I renounce
him. Yet have I from him poesy, a boon of price. I shall wait,
nor fear death."

I

M UCH doth it task me
My tongue to move,
Through my throat to utter
The breath of song.

Poesy, prize of Odin,
Promise now I may not,
A draught drawn not lightly
From deep thought's dwelling.

2

Forth it flows but hardly;
For within my breast
Heavy sobbing stifles
Hindered stream of song—
Blessèd boon to mortals
Brought from Odin's kin,
Goodly treasure, stolen
From Giant-land of yore.

3

He, who so blameless
Bore him in life,
O'erborne by billows
With boat was whelmed.
Sea-waves—flood that whilom
Welled from giant's wound—
Smite upon the grave-gate
Of my sire and son.

4

Dwindling now my kindred
Draw near to their end,
Ev'n as forest-saplings
Felled or tempest-strown.
Not gay or gladsome
Goes he who beareth
Body of kinsman
On funeral bier.

5

Of a father fallen
First I may tell ;
Of a much-loved mother
Must mourn the loss.
Sad store hath memory
For minstrel skill,
A wood to bloom leafy
With words of song.

6

Most woful the breach,
Where the wave in-brake
On the fencèd hold
Of my father's kin.

Unfilled, as I wot,
And open doth stand
The gap of son rent
By the greedy surge.

7

Me Ran, the sea-queen,
Roughly hath shaken :
I stand of beloved ones
Stript and all bare.
Cut hath the billow
The cord of my kin,
Strand of mine own twisting
So stout and strong.

8

Sure, if sword could venge
Such cruel wrong,
Evil times would wait
Ægir, ocean-god.
That wind-giant's brother
Were I strong to slay,
'Gainst him and his sea-brood
Battling would I go.

9

But I in no wise
Boast, as I ween,
Strength that may strive
With the stout ships' bane.
For to eyes of all
Easy now 'tis seen
How the old man's lot
Helpless is and lone.

10

Me hath the main
Of much bereaved ;
Dire is the tale,
The deaths of kin :
Since he, the shelter
And shield of my house,
Hied him from life
To heaven's glad realm.

11

Full surely I know,
In my son was waxing
The stuff and the strength
Of a stout-limbed wight :

Had he reached but ripeness
To raise his shield,
And Odin laid hand
On his liegeman true.

12

Willing he followed
His father's word,
Though all opposing
Should thwart my rede:
He in mine household
Mine honour upheld,
Of my power and rule
The prop and the stay.

13

Oft to my mind
My loss doth come,
How I brotherless bide
Bereaved and lone.
Thereon I bethink me,
When thickens the fight!
Thereon with much searching
My soul doth muse:

14

Who staunch stands by me
In stress of fight,
Shoulder to shoulder,
Side by side ?
Such want doth weaken
In war's dread hour ;
Weak-winged I fly,
Whom friends all fail.

15

"Son's place to his sire
(Saith a proverb true)
Another son born
Alone can fill."
Of kinsmen none
(Though ne'er so kind)
To brother can stand
In brother's stead.

16

O'er all our ice-fields,
Our northern snows,
Few now I find
Faithful and true.

Dark deeds men love,
Doom death to their kin,
A brother's body
Barter for gold.

17

Unpleasing to me
Our people's mood,
Each seeking his own
In selfish peace.
To the happier bees' home
Hath passed my son,
My good wife's child
To his glorious kin.

18

Odin, mighty monarch,
Of minstrel mead the lord,
On me a heavy hand
Harmful doth lay.
Gloomy in unrest
Ever I grieve,
Sinks my drooping brow,
Seat of sight and thought.

19

Fierce fire of sickness
First from my home
Swept off a son
With savage blow :
One who was heedful,
Harmless, I wot,
In deeds unblemished,
In words unblamed.

20

Still do I mind me,
When the Friend of men
High uplifted
To the home of gods
That sapling stout
Of his father's stem,
Of my true wife born
A branch so fair.

21

Once bare I goodwill
To the great spear-lord,
Him trusty and true
I trowed for friend :

Till the giver of conquest,
The car-borne god,
Broke faith and friendship,
False in my need.

22

Now victim and worship
To Vilir's brother,
The god once honoured,
I give no more.
Yet the friend of Mimir
On me hath bestowed
Some boot for bale,
If all boons I tell.

23

Yea he, the wolf-tamer,
The war-god skilful,
Gave poesy faultless
To fill my soul :
Gave wit to know well
Each wily trickster,
And force him to face me
As foeman in fight.

24

Hard am I beset ;
Whom Hel, the sister
Of Odin's fell captive,
On Digra-ness waits.
Yet shall I gladly
With right good welcome
Dauntless in bearing
Her death-blow bide.

ARINBJORN'S EPIC

Arinbjorn, Egil's noble and faithful friend, appears often in the Egilssaga. He spent the evening of his life in Norway in great honour. Egil composed a poem in his praise; of which what we have is said to be "the beginning." It seems fairly complete, though three stanzas are defective. But it may well have been much longer: more might have been said about Arinbjorn's war-like expeditions. Sixty stanzas is said to have been a not un-usual length for a *drápa*, or heroic poem: this, as will be seen, only extends to twenty-six.

I

FOR generous prince
    Swift praise I find,
But stint my words
To stingy churl.
Openly sing I
Of king's true deeds,
But silence keep
On slander's lies.

2

For fabling braggarts
Full am I of scorn,
But willing speak I
Of worthy friends:
Courts I of monarchs
A many have sought,
A gallant minstrel
Of guileless mood.

3

Erewhile the anger
Of Yngling's son
I bore, prince royal
Of race divine.
With hood of daring
O'er dark locks drawn
A lord right noble
I rode to seek.

4

There sate in might
The monarch strong,
With helm of terror
High-throned and dread;

A king unbending,
With bloody blade,
Within York city
Wielded he power.

5

That moon-like brightness
Might none behold,
Nor brook undaunted
Great Eric's brow:
As fiery serpent
His flashing eyes
Shot starry radiance
Stern and keen.

6

Yet I to this ruler
Of fishful seas
My bolster-mate's ransom
Made bold to bear,
Of Odin's goblet
O'erflowing dew
Each listening ear-mouth
Eagerly drank,

7

Not beauteous in seeming
My bardic fee
To ranks of heroes
In royal hall:
When I my hood-knoll,
Wolf-gray of hue,
For mead of Odin
From monarch gat.

8

Thankful I took it,
And therewithal
The pit-holes black
Of my beetling brows;
Yea, and that mouth
That for me bare
The poem of praise
To princely knees.

9

Tooth-fence took I,
And tongue likewise,
Ears' sounding chambers
And sheltering eaves.

And better deemed I
Than brightest gold
The gift then given
By glorious king.

10

There a staunch stay
Stood by my side,
One man worth many
Of meaner wights,
Mine own true friend
Whom trusty I found,
High-couraged ever
In counsels bold.

11

Arinbjorn
Alone us saved—
Foremost of champions—
From fury of king;
Friend of the monarch
He framed no lies
Within that palace
Of warlike prince.

12

Of the stay of our house
Still spake he truth,
(While much he honoured
My hero-deeds)
Of the son of Kveldulf,
Whom fair-haired king
Slew for a slander,
But honoured slain.

13

Wrong were it if he
Who wrought me good,
Gold-spender lavish,
Such gifts had cast
To the wasteful tract
Of the wild sea-mew,
To the surge rough-ridden
By sea-kings' steeds.

14

False to my friend
Were I fairly called,
An untrue steward
Of Odin's cup;

Of praise unworthy,
Pledge-breaker vile,
If I for such good
Gave nought again.

15

Now better seeth
The bard to climb
With feet poetic
The frowning steep,
And set forth open
In sight of all
The laud and honour
Of high-born chief.

16

Now shall my voice-plane
Shape into song
Virtues full many
Of valiant friend.
Ready on tongue
Twofold they lie,
Yea, threefold the praises
Of Thorir's son.

17

First tell I forth
What far is known,
Openly bruited
In ears of all;
How generous of mood
Men deem this lord,
Bjorn of the hearth-fire
The birchwood's bane.

18

Folk bear witness
With wond'ring praise,
How to all guests
Good gifts he gives:
For Bjorn of the hearth-stone
Is blest with store
Freely and fully
By Frey and Njord.

19

To him, high scion
Of Hroald's tree,
Fulness of riches
Flowing hath come;

And friends ride thither
In thronging crowd
By all wide ways
'Neath windy heaven.

20

Above his ears
Around his brow
A coronal fair,
As a king, he wore.
Beloved of gods,
Beloved of men,
The warrior's friend,
The weakling's aid.

21

That mark he hitteth
That most men miss;
Though money they gather,
This many lack:
For few be the bounteous
And far between,
Nor easily shafted
Are all men's spears.

22

Out of the mansion
Of Arinbjorn,
When guested and rested
In generous wise,
None with hard jest,
None with rude jeer,
None with his axe-hand
Ungifted hied.

23

Hater of money
Is he of the Firths,
A foe to the gold-drops
Of Draupnir born.

.   .   .

24

Rings he scatters,
Riches he squanders,
Of avarice thievish
An enemy still.

.   .   .

25

Long course of life
His lot hath been,
Broken by battles,
Bereft of peace.

.   .   .

26

Early waked I,
Words I gathered,
Toiled each morning
With speech-moulding tongue.
A proud pile built I
Of praise long-lasting,
To stand unbroken
In Bragi's town.

FROM NJAL'S SAGA

GUNNAR'S DEFENCE

Gunnar, forced into quarrels by Hallgerda his wife, is attacked
by his foes and slain.

UP started Gunnar from his sleep, as a weird and
 woful sound
Rang through the silence.   " 'Twas thy cry, my grey,
 my guardian hound!
Surely foul play is on thee wrought: and 'twixt us
 twain, I ween,
Will be short space; who kill the dog to kill the
 master mean."
 But wherefore then hath Gunnar foes, Gunnar
 the stout and strong,
Yet kind and courteous past compare, no worker he
 of wrong?

Gunnar the pride of the country-side? A fair false
 ill-wed wife
Drove him on bloodshed and on broils, and now will
 spill his life.
Of deaths that he unwilling dealt (for none before
 him stood)
He willing paid awarded fines and made atonement
 good :
And winters three by Thing's decree he now abroad
 must stay,
Or him with right as outlaw'd wight the slain man's
 kin might slay.
The ship lies freighted; toward the bay Gunnar and
 Kolskegg ride,
True brothers they, adown the dale, along the river-
 side :
When sudden stumbles Gunnar's steed, and throws
 him, that his eyes
Turned upward gaze on the fell and the farm that at
 the fell-foot lies.
" Fair shows the fell, as never yet ; white waves the
 corn, green glow
Our new-mown meads.   Back will I ride, nor wander-
 ing forth will go."

He spake: his brother urged him sore not thus his foes
 to please,
Nor slight Njal's warning words: "To thee this
 voyage beyond the seas
Works honour, praise, and length of days; but, an thy
 terms thou break,
I do foresee swift death to thee, friends sorrowing for
 thy sake."
But Gunnar heard not. Then abroad fared Kolskegg,
 nevermore
Fated to see his brother's face, or tread dear Iceland's
 shore.
 So wilful Gunnar sat at home. But his foemen
 gathered rede,
And banded them, full forty men (nor of one less was
 need
For such emprize), and to Lithe-end they took their
 stealthy way,
And by a neighbour Thorkell's help the hound they
 lure and slay.
Forty they were: among them chief rode Gizur,
 named the White,
With Geir the priest, and Thorleik's sons, and Mord
 of guileful spite,

Two Aununds, Thorgrim Easterling, and many more
    who burn
For the fell deed, yet few thereout all scatheless should
    return.
    Wood-wrought was Gunnar's hall; clinched boards
    from roof-ridge doubly sloped;
Where wall met roof, there window-slits with screen-
    ing shutters oped:
Above the ceiling of the hall were lofts: himself slept
    there,
Hallgerda, and his mother—three. For his foes with
    coward care
Learnt his farm-folk were all afield, nor, ere the hound
    was still,
Two score upon one man dared come to work their
    wicked will.
    Gunnar awoke at the dog's death-howl; but his
    foemen nought could hear,
Nor know for sure were he within: so Thorgrim
    drew anear
To spy and list. He clomb the wall, and soon his
    kirtle red
To Gunnar at a window show'd. Forth lunged that
    weapon dread

The bill, and smote him in the waist.   Slipped Thor-
    grim's feet, his shield

Dropt loose, he tumbled from the eaves.   With much
    ado he reeled

To where with Gizur sat the rest.   " Is he at home,
    our foe ? "

They ask.   Quoth Thorgrim, " 'Tis for you how that
    may be to know :

This know I, that his bill's at home."   Dead fell he
    speaking so.

Upon the dead they looked not long.   Sure of their
    prey within

Trapped in his lair, right at the house they rushed, in
    hope to win

Entrance by window, wall, or door : when from the
    eaves forth came

Arrow on arrow, wheresoe'er assailant showed, with
    aim

Unerring.   Nought their might prevails.   Some seek
    th' outbuildings' screen,

Thence safelier to attack ; but still e'en there the
    arrows keen

Find them, nor doth their errand speed.   And so
    with efforts vain
They strive awhile, then draw they off to rest and
    charge again.
With rage redoubled they return, shoot, batter, hew,
    and climb ;
But still the dread bow hurls its hail, until a second
    time
They back recoil.   Then Gizur cried, "We must our
    onset make
With wiser heed, or nothing we by this our ride shall
    take."
So again they fight with a steadier might and an
    onslaught tough and long,
But a third time cower from the arrowy shower of
    Gunnar stout and strong.
  And haply now they had given o'er with wounds
    and labour spent,
But for a chance that to their troop new heart and
    courage lent.
Upon the ledge of wall without Gunnar an arrow
    spied.
"An arrow of theirs !   'Twill shame them well," so
    spake he in his pride,

"From their own shaft to suffer scathe."   "My son,
    nay do not so,
Rouse not the slack," his mother said ; "they waver,
    let them go."
But Gunnar drew it in, and shot, and with that arrow
    keen
Smote sorely Eylif Aunund's son, yet did it not un-
    seen.
"Ha !" Gizur said, "out came a hand a golden ring
    that wore,
And plucked an arrow from the roof.   If of such wood
    were store
At home, it were not sought abroad.   With hope
    renewed set on ;
Not Gunnar's self can hold us off when all his shafts
    are gone."
Then out spake Mord amid them all, the man of
    guileful ways :
"Fire we the house, and at no cost burn Gunnar in
    the blaze."
"No by my honour," Gizur said, "that deed shall
    never be·—
Such craven work—not though my life lay on it.
    And for thee

Some counsel that may serve our need 'twere easy
    sure to frame,
So cunning as thou art; or is thy cunning but in
    name?"
Awhile Mord pondered, till he marked where lay
    upon the ground
Some coilèd ropes, wherewith the house in strengthen-
    ing bands they bound
Ofttimes; for joist and plank and beam such girding
    needed well,
When whirling wind and furious storm drove sweep-
    ing down the fell.
"These ropes," quoth Mord, " o'er the jutting ends
    of the bearing beams we'll cast,
And to the sturdy rocks hard by the other ends make
    fast,
Then with windlass strain and twist amain, until
    from off the hall
Following perforce the tightened cord the yielding
    roof shall fall."
All praise the rede, all lend their hands; and, ere the
    chief was ware,
Off slid the roof, and to the skies the gaping lofts lay
    bare.

Fierce then his foes on Gunnar swarm, not hidden as
    before,
And climb and strike and hurl and shoot; but still
    his arrows pour
This way and that, where'er they charge, and though
    each shift they try,
Despite of numbers they are foiled and cannot come
    anigh.
So doth the lordly boar at bay deal havoc 'mid the
    hounds,
His lightning tusks full many a side gashing with
    gory wounds.
"Waste we not lives, but burn the hall, I said, and
    say again,"
Quoth Mord; but Gizur, much in wrath, "Why
    thou what none are fain
To follow bidst, I know not, I; but this shall ne'er
    be done."
Just then upon the side roof leapt bold Thorbrand,
    Thorleik's son;
Who, as with other aim averse Gunnar his string
    back-drew,
Reached from behind and deftly cut the tightened
    sinew through.

Gunnar with both hands clutched his bill, turned
    quick, and Thorbrand thrust

With such a forceful stroke that he down toppled in
    the dust.

Asbrand, his brother, sprang to aid; but from the
    wall was dashed

With broken arms, as through his shield the bill
    resistless crashed.

And now had Gunnar wounded eight, and two out-
    right had slain,

Himself received two wounds, but nought recked he
    of wounds or pain,

Unflinching still through blows and ill, till treachery
    wrought his bane.

"Take of thy hair two locks; therewith shalt thou
    and mother mine,"

Thus Gunnar to Hallgerda spake, "another bow-
    string twine."

"Lies aught at stake on this?" said she. But he,
    "At stake my life;

For while my bow to reach them serves, to come to
    closer strife

They'll get no chance."   And she again, "Remem-
    ber now the blow
Thou gav'st me once upon the cheek.   As for thy
    life, I trow,
I care not be it short or long."   Said Gunnar, "Of
    his deed
Each earns due glory; for this boon with thee no
    more I plead."
But bitterly burst Rannveig out, "And shall such
    hero die
For a slap well dealt to a thievish slut in wrath at
    her thievery?
O wicked and unwifely thou!   Long shall endure
    thy shame,
And Iceland's children yet unborn shall curse Hall-
    gerda's name!"
  Then round him close his vengeful foes, yet still
    he wards them well,
And he strook eight more with blows full sore and
    nigh to death, then fell
Weary and worn.   Their fallen foe they do not
    spare to smite,
Who yet defends him and past hope prolongs a losing
    fight,

Baffling each hand of the caitiff band, until at length
    that crew,
Forty on one, with stroke on stroke the noble Gunnar
    slew.

Thus Gunnar died; but died not thus the fame of
    Hamond's son,—
It lives upon the mouth of skalds, his deeds due meed
    have won.
For in that arctic isle of ice, that world of wonders
    strange,
Where frost and fire twin empire hold, and in con-
    trasted change
Drear Jökuls tower and frown above and meadows
    smile below,
And over molten rocks and sand the snow-fed torrents
    go,
There, long as Hecla nurses flame and bubbling
    geysers steam,
And the white sheep dot the pastures, and the salmon
    leap in the stream,

Of sturdy sires Icelandic bards shall ever love to
    tell
Brave blow, fierce fight, rough ride, mad leap, wild
    feats by fiord and fell.
  A truer faith, a milder mood, now rules that
    northern land;
Vengeance then burned in every heart, vengeance
    armed every hand;
Blood blood-begotten blood begat, and broil was born
    of broil,
And kindred feuds ran evil round in never-ending
    coil.
Yet deeds of courtesy were there no less than deeds of
    rage;
And Gunnar peerless shone in all, and better than
    his age.
So we, with kinder skies and laws in weaklier times
    who live,
All honour due to the valour true of a ruder race
    may give.
And still, when winter's night is long beneath the
    circling Bear,
When few are afield and many at home, and by the
    warm fire's glare

The women weave or knit or spin, while to refresh
    the task
The story and the song go round, oft will a maiden
    ask,
"Tell us the tale that never tires to ears Icelandic
    told,
How Gunnar guarded well his hall, how dear his life
    he sold."

SKARPHEDINN'S LEAP (c. 91)

NjAL's sons, being warned of the approach of certain foemen, go
out to meet them.   Their encounter is here told.

"NOW whither away?" quoth father Njal,
    "My sons, O whither away?"
"A-hunting we fare," Skarphedinn said,
    "For a sheep that hath gone astray."

"So saidst thou once, thine errand to cloke,
    So say'st thou yet again :
But thy war-axe rang on my panel this morn ;
    Ye hunt not sheep, but men."

Skarphedinn he laugh'd, and the brothers five
    Went forth well-weapon'd and dight,
And they bent their course to the riverside
    That morning fair and bright.

For foemen had been seen hard by,
  Who home that way would ride.
Scorning to hide them, in open field
  Njal's sons their coming will bide.

Bitter the taunts those spiteful foes
  On their father and kin had cast:
The day of reckoning (so they deem)
  Hath surely come at last.

'Twas Thrain the son of Sigfus,
  And Hrapp of killing fame,
With Gunnar brother's son to Thrain,
  And other five, that came.

As down the dale they travel,
  They spy the sun's bright beam
Reflected from the shields of men
  Afar beyond the stream.

" Now turn we from our road" said Thrain,
  " Close down to the shore of Fleet:
If these with us have errand,
  They'll haste our path to meet."

Nearer they drew. "They are but five,"
  Said Thrain, "and we twice four."
Quoth Lambi, "Nay, the sons of Njal
  Will brave these odds or more."

Fleet with his wintry waters
  Was rolling deep and strong,
And sheets of shelving ice-bank
  Edged either shore along.

Unfordable that eddying flood,
  . But here and there a band
Of frosted crystal with frail bridge
  The darkling torrent spann'd.

As down they ran, those sons of Njal,
  Skarphedinn's shoe-thong brake;
He stoop'd to bind: the rest press on,
  And for an ice-bridge make.

Skarphedinn soon rose ready:
  Lo, right against him stood
Thrain's warriors on an ice-field
  That stretch'd along the flood.

The bridge, he saw, was well-nigh gain'd
   By Kari and the rest:
Time fails (he thought) to follow round,
   The nearest way is best.

Straight down he ran, and strongly he sprang
   With leap both wide and high;
From ice to ice he bounded,
   And, swift as hawk may fly,

Skimm'd o'er the slippery crystal,
   Nor checking aught his course
His lifted battle-axe on Thrain
   Brought down with fatal force.

And onward still he glided,
   Before th' astonied foe—
As past and from them on he flash'd—
   Might reach him with a blow.

At the far end o' th' ice-sheet
   He turned him back again;
With him his brothers. Short the fight:
   Their foes to yield were fain.

Thrain, Hrapp, and Tjorvi fell : the rest
  From generous foes took life.
(Life that two thankless churls abused
  To stir more deathful strife)

Said Kari, " Measure we the gulf
  Whereo'er Skarphedinn flew ;
From bank to bank such breadth to clear
  Is given, I ween, to few."

Twelve Norway ells their spear-shafts showed
  That gap across the deep.
Men gaze to-day, and marvel much
  At bold Skarphedinn's leap.

THE BURNING OF NJAL (*c.* 127)

I

STEADILY gallop on Skeidará sand
   Westwards to Woodcombe a weaponed band:
Dismounting at Kirby to kirk they repair,
But short their leisure for thrift or prayer:
"To horse!" is the word; and up the fell steep
Again unresting their course they keep,
Till Fishwater lakes on the right hand gleam;
Then westwards they turn them down glen and
      stream.
And Eyjafell Jökul his mass doth show
To their left, as o'er Mœlifell's sand they go.
Soon Goda-land gaining and Markfleet's tide
Upwards to Three-corner ridge they ride;
There reining their steeds they stay their race,
For Three-corner hill was their trysting-place.

2

Betimes on the Lord's Day they busked them from
    home,
At nones of the second the ridge they clomb.
What errand so urges, that night and day
In the drear late autumn they speed their way?
They speed not to wedding, to farm or to field,
Nor summoned to Thing-mote. With sword and
    with shield
Well-weaponed they ride, and their faces stern
Speak hearts within that for grim work burn.
They wait on the hill till at even-fall
From many a homestead were gathered all,
Six score, who on forfeit of life and land
Were sworn in this quarrel together to stand.

3

But who are their foes in this feud of blood?
The sons of Njal, of Njal the good.
Wisest and gentlest was he, I trow,
Of Iceland's sages long ago;
Well-learnèd in laws, in counsel kind,
Foreseeing with more than mortal mind.

Three sons he begat, sons tall and strong;
And Skarphedinn the eldest was bitter of tongue.
Fain then of blow was an Icelander's hand;
Ready for battle an Icelander's brand:
Rough was the age; and in quarrels fell
Njal's sons had borne them so stoutly and well,
That from every bout unscathed they came,
And many for kinsfolk killed made claim.
Njal still sought peace, would heal each strife;
But hot was hatred, and slanders rife.
Atonements fixed and the Thing's award
Skarphedinn with gibe and taunt had marred:
Blood now the avengers' thirst must slake,
For blood this tryst on the hill they make.

4

Flosi rode chief, wise wight and stark;
Beside him Kettle, lord of the Mark;
Backed full bravely by brothers four,
The sons of Sigfus, men of power;
There rode great Gunnar's son, in spite
Eager and cruel, but craven in fight.
There many more of lesser name,
Whom kindred blood or friendship's claim

Or envy stirred to lend their blade
And join them to the murderous raid.

5

At Bergthors-knoll the board was cleared,
Yet slept they not: for tidings were heard
Of faring and flitting of man and horse
All one way bent, as of gathering force.
And Grim and Helgi had homeward sped
(As the mother Bergthora boding said),
And wondering Njal saw vision dire
Of gaping gable and flaming fire.
All told of fate and foemen nigh,
Yet held they still their courage high,
Three brothers, and Kari, than brother not less,
And true men staunch to aid their stress.

6

"They come?" is the cry.   From the ridge they
    had ridden,
Their steeds in the dell they had tethered and hidden ;
And now advancing steady and slow
A firm and well-knit band they show.

But awhile they halt, when they see in the yard
Of stalwart defenders so ready a guard.
Spake Flosi: "Despite our numbers strong,
This battle may be both tough and long,
If fought in the open: such price we shall pay
That few shall tell who won the day.
Though they be thirty, twice threescore we,
There are champions among them well worth three:
While some who most keenly our quarrel stirred
Will be backward in deed as forward in word."

7

Skarphedinn marked their parleying stay:
"They deem us," quoth he, "no easy prey
Thus warned and armed."   "Rather defend
The house within: he of Lithe-end,
Brave Gunnar, alone foiled forty so:
To seek close quarters these will be slow."
Thus Njal, for once the weaker way
Choosing.   Skarphedinn answered: "Yea;
But generous foes on Gunnar came,
To win by fire they thought foul shame.
Far other these.   Bent on our bane
No means they'll spare their end to gain."

Then Helgi spake: " Brother, 'twere ill
To cross our wise old father's will."
" Nay," quoth Skarphedinn; "the wise man *fey*
May prove unwise.   But I obey.
Fox-like to stifle ill suits my breath;
Yet burn we together, I fear not death."
So entered they, lured to their doom,
The house that soon should be their tomb.

8

" Now are they ours! " said Flosi glad;
" Men soon to die choose counsels mad.
With all our speed press we straight on,
Beset and throng the door, let none
Break forth.   And compass every side,
Lest other issue forth be tried,
Postern or wicket.   'Twere our bane,
Vengeance were sure, our work were vain,
Should one alone of the brothers three
Or Kari their sister's lord go free."

9

So Flosi with his best in front
Charged onwards, where, to bear the brunt,

Two champions in the doorway stood,
And first Skarphedinn's axe drank blood.
At him with mighty spear-thrust dashed
Bold Hroald, Auzur's son.   Down flashed
The Battle-ogress blade, and hewed
The spear-head off; then, quick renewed,
A second blow beat down the shield
And cleft his brow: he tottering reeled,
And backward at full length lay dead.
"Small chance had that one," Kari said.

10

Fierce was the onslaught, stern the play
Of thrust and blow: to force their way
Th' assailants strove, but no advance
Could make, for frequent shaft and lance
Flew forth, and many quailed before
The dauntless pair who kept the door,
By Grim and Helgi backed.   Nor found
They who close hemmed the house around
Inlet or opening; firm and sure
The stronghold doth their rage endure.

11

At last spake Flosi : "From our foes
We win but wounds ; one slain we loose
Whom least we would.   By sword and spear
Methinks we force not entrance here.
And some who egged us on the most
Are dull with blow though loud in boast.
Two choices have we, to return,
Or house and all within to burn.
Death were the issue sure of one ;
The other were a deed ill done
By Christian men, a grievous deed,
Yet must we do it in our need."

12

So they gather wood, and a pile they make
Before the doors, and fire they take
And set thereto ; but the women-folk
Throw whey or water, and quench in smoke,
Fast as the foemen light, till one—
Kol was he namèd, Thorstein's son—
Espied of chickweed dry a stack
Against the house close to the back

Upon the hill-slope. "Light we this,
To pass the fire we cannot miss
Into the lofts above the hall;
Soon will the cross-trees burn and fall."
He spake: 'twas done; and, ere they know,
The roof above is all aglow.

13

Then 'gan the women to wail and to weep,
But Njal spake comfort, and bade them keep
Good courage all. "This storm once past,
Ye shall," he said, "find rest at last.
Trust Him who still to save is near."
These spake he and other words of cheer.
But yet more widely overhead
The creeping flames their ruin spread.

14

Now to the door went Njal, and cried,
"Can Flosi hear?" "Yea," he replied.
"Wilt from my sons atonement take?"
Said Njal; "or wilt thou for my sake
Let any men go forth?" But he:
"Thy sons for no price shall go free;

Till they be dead I stir not, I;
This ends our dealings, when they die.
But with women and children we wage no strife,
They and the house-carles may go with life."

15

"Now go, Thorhalla, thou, and they
To whom 'tis given, go while ye may."
So Njal. "We part, thy son and I,
Not as we thought; yet will I try,"
She said, "if haply a loyal wife
May vengeance win for a husband's life."
But Astrid, wife of Grim, "E'en yet
Thy lord may 'scape: such foes are met
Rightly by fraud; come, Helgi, thou
Come forth with me: with cloak, I trow,
And kerchief on thy head for dress,
Thou'lt pass for woman in the press."
Such guile misliked him, but their prayer
Prevailed at last, and forth they fare.
But Flosi marked, "Tall is that dame
And broad of shoulders, take the same
And hold her." Helgi cast the cloak,
Hewed down one foeman with a stroke,

Then stricken by great Flosi's blade
With severed head in dust was laid.

16

Again to th' entrance Flosi came,
"Good father Njal," he cried, "'twere shame
That thou shouldst guiltless burn; I give
Thee egress free,—come out and live."
"Not so," said Njal, "for I am old,
To venge my sons nor fit nor bold,
But will not live disgraced."   "Thou, then,
Housewife," cried Flosi once again;
"Come out, Bergthora, for no sake
Would I thy life thus cruel take."
"Nay, Njal was husband of my youth,"
Said she; "I promised in all truth
One fate we both would alway share."
So turned they back, that faithful pair.

17

"What counsel now?" Bergthora said.
"We will lie down upon our bed,"
Said Njal; "for rest I long have craved."
"But first," said she, "thou must be saved,

Dear grandchild Thord, nor here be burned."
"Dear minnie mine," the boy returned,
"Thou promisedst that 'gainst my will
Ne'er should I leave thee.   Life were ill
After you dead: far rather I
Choose me with Njal and thee to die."

18

She bore him with a gentle smile
Toward the bed; and Njal the while
Spake to his steward: "Bear in mind
How we do place us, so thou'lt find
Our bones hereafter; I nor turn
Nor flinch for reek or smart or burn.
See'st thou yon ox-hide?   O'er us spread
That covering as we lie abed.
This done, go forth, and make good haste
To save thee living while thou mayst."
So down they lay, the loving pair,
With the lad between: they breathed a prayer,
Made sign of cross, nor stir nor word
Thereafter from that couch was heard.
"Age is soon weary," Skarphedinn said,
"Our father and mother go early to bed."

19

Fiercer and fiercer the red flames roar,
Burning fragments bestrew the floor,
Hotter and hotter the stifling air,
But a brave heart still those brothers bear,
Skarphedinn and Grim, and Kari withal;
And fast as the firebrands sparkling fall,
Scornful they fling them abroad on their foes,
Who pitiless wait the cruel close.
No more they shoot on the men within;
" On them with weapons no fame we win,"
Said Flosi; " stand we but idle by,
Fire gains us a sure sad victory."

20

Now nigh the hall-end fell a beam,
Slanting across.   Of hope a gleam
Saw Kari: " Climb we by this," said he,
" Then leap, and haply we may go free.
For hitherward is blown the smoke,
And that may well our venture cloke.
And leap thou first."   " Brother, not so;
Upon thy heels I'll following go."

"That were unwise; this weakened wood
To bear thee then will scarce hold good;
But I, though I be balked of this,
Some other outlet will not miss."
So Kari; but Skarphedinn said
Unmoved, "Go thou, and venge me dead."

21

Then Kari ran up the beam that spanned
From floor to wall, and bore in hand
A burning bench, and flung outside
His burden.   The nearest scattered them wide,
As it fell in their midst, and Kari aglow
In clothes and hair they might not know,
As down from the wall he nimbly leapt:
Then stealthily with the smoke he crept
And gained a stream, there plunging quenched
The flames upon him, and issuing drenched
Sped on smoke-screened, till in hollow ground
Safe hiding awhile and rest he found.

22

Skarphedinn up the frail bridge sped
With unlike hap; for 'neath his tread

The burnt beam snapt; yet did he fall
Upon his feet, and at the wall
Leapt grappling, and had wellnigh scaled
The top, when crackling timbers failed
And with him toppled.   "What must be,"
He said, "'tis easy now to see."

23

Two brothers alone in life remain,
Skarphedinn and Grim.   Awhile the twain
Together trode the fiery floor,
Till Grim sank down to rise no more.
Then sought Skarphedinn the gable end,
Where soon the roof down crashing penned
His prisoned steps.   Nor thence he stirred,
Nor sound or groan of pain was heard;
There stern and soldier-like he stood
Beside his axe, that in the wood
Of gable wall was driven deep,—
Erect he met his deathful sleep.

24

'Tis dawn.   Behold a dreary scene!
Where life and health and stir have been,

There crumbling walls half-burnt and bare
Gape roofless to the chilly air.
The floor within, the ground without,
With relics charred are strown about.
Embers still glowing, ashes grey,
While here and there in garish day
The paler flames with fitful greed
On fuel fresh unsated feed.
Sad scene!   Too well the vengeful crew
Have done the deed they sware to do.
Stillness is here, but not of peace;
Blood-feuds by bloodshed do not cease.
Burners, beware! the seed ye sow
Shall to a heavy harvest grow;
On those who slew the good and wise,
All Iceland loud for vengeance cries.

25

Anon men searched the ruined hall,
And gathered bones for burial.
Of nine that perished remains they found,
And duly laid in hallowed ground.
Skarphedinn stood, e'en as he died,
At the hall-end, and by his side

His axe: scarce burnt by fire his corse—
The planks had screened the flames' full force.
Where Njal and dame Bergthora lay,
Deep ashes first they dug away,
Then 'neath them saw the tough ox-hide,
Shrivelled by fire it was and dried;
But when they lifted it, the pair
Lay all unburnt and fresh and fair,
They and the lad: and, wondrous sight,
Njal's face and body shone so bright,
Men said such marvel never had been,
Never in death such beauty seen.
A token sure of better days
To come ere long, and milder ways,
When truer faith o'er Iceland spread
Should mercy set in vengeance' stead,
Nor Njal have perished all in vain,
A gentle wight ungently slain.

THE RECONCILIATION OF FLOSI
AND KARI (*c.* 158)

FLOSI at Swinefell dwelt in peace. Atonement
    he had made,
Fulfill'd all terms as bade the laws, all blood-fines
    duly paid,
Abroad had wandered three long years, had south-
    ward fared to Rome,
To the holy father knelt for shrift; then sought his
    northern home.
Tho' leader in an ill deed once, of noble heart was he,
And now life's restful eve would spend from guilt and
    quarrel free.

Njal's burning cost the burners dear. Vengeance had
    overta'en
That vengeful crew. First, at the Thing, in fight
    were many slain,

Exiled the rest: whom o'er the seas an evil hap
    pursued.
In Brian's battle Erin's soil drank deep their outpour'd
    blood;
Where fell thrice five, whence one alive Icelandic
    shores regain'd;
And soon or late by various fate their dwindling
    numbers waned.

But chiefly Kari wrought their bane; whom a just
    fortune sped
Unscathed thro' flames and foes to 'scape and venge
    Skarphedinn dead.
Remembering still that brother's death to whom he
    owed his life,
Remembering still his child's sad fate, he vow'd
    relentless strife.
"Never," said he, "my hand shall fail, never my
    heart forget,
Till lives of men, not lands or fines, have paid the
    heavy debt.

Nor idle vow he spake: for still, to his set purpose true,
At home, abroad, he smote his foes, yet fairly smote
    and slew.

Nay dared against great risk and odds.   Witness in
    Orkney's isle,
When at Earl Sigurd's Yule-tide feast, the drinking
    to beguile,
The story of the Burning told by crafty Lambi's son
Held hush'd the list'ning guests.   He told how the
    fell deed was done ;
But falsely told that in the fire Skarphedinn soften'd
    wept,
Adding to lies loud laugh and jeer.

               Then with drawn sword in leapt
Kari, whom fate had thither brought those lies to
    overhear,
Rush'd up the hall, and with one blow on the caitiff
    neck did shear
His sever'd head, that spinning fell the king and earls
    before,
And the table long and the festal throng were all
    besprent with gore.

"Seize Kari, slay him," cried the earl.   But not a
    man upstood ;
"My lord," quoth Kari, "I but venge thy henchman
    Helgi's blood."

And Flosi, "That false throat, sir earl, Kari did well
    to smite:
Between us no atonement stands: he hath herein full
    right."
Kari strode forth unharmed.   Spake then king
    Sigtrygg, "Bold, I trow,
That wight, nor thought he twice who dealt that
    stout unwavering blow."
"Yea verily, for daring dash," Earl Sigurd quick
    returns,
"None matcheth Kari since Lithe-end its peerless
    Gunnar mourns."

But Kari sought his trusty mates, and spread his
    wand'ring sails
For other shores.   Scotland his strength and prowess
    learn'd, and Wales.
At length, the Burning dearly venged, weary of
    bloody broil,
A humble pilgrim south he fared afoot to Latin soil,
Was shrived, and homeward set his face.   In Nor-
    mandy again
His ship he took: the western coast he compass'd,
    braved the main

Where Scotland's firths far-branching pierce her
 mountain-crownéd shore,
Doubled the Cape of Wrath, and pass'd fierce Pent-
 land's race and roar.

Six years were spent since that sad eve on which the
 Burners' raid
Njal's homestead fair at Bergthorsknoll in cinder'd
 ruins laid.
Kari from Caithness busk'd him late to sail an
 autumn sea :
Helga was dead, a widower lone a wifeless home
 sought he.
Slow voyage they made by gales delay'd, till to their
 lab'ring bark
Iceland's east bluff o'er waters rough loom'd dangerous
 and dark.
'Twas Ingolf's Head, no haven this, but rocks and
 dashing wave :
Shiver'd and rent their ship was lost, themselves they
 scarce might save.
What counsel now ?   " Swine-fell is nigh"; said
 Kari, " there doth bide
Flosi mine ancient foe.   Lo now his manhood shall
 be tried."

So in rain and wind sore drench'd and blind to
    Swine-fell up they fare,
Despite of ill undaunted still to suffer or to dare.

Flosi sat restful in his hall, with hearth-fires burning
    bright,
His folk among. Sudden stept in a stormbeat way-
    worn wight:
Whom Flosi knew at once, and swift upsprang the
    man to meet,
Fell on his neck, and kiss'd him there, and to the
    honoured seat
Beside him led. "O welcome thou, whilom my foe,
    now friend!
Pardon and peace we both have sought, our feud hath
    here its end.
No further roam, here in my home freely of what is
    mine
Shelter and food and greeting good I give to thee
    and thine."

Thus hate was heal'd and love was knit and peace
    o'ermaster'd strife;
And Hildigunna, Flosi's kin, with Kari match'd as
    wife.

And in their children's children yet, who noble fame
    have won,
Live Burning Flosi of Swinefell and Kari Solmund's
    son.

FROM THE SAGA OF GUNNLAUG SNAKE-TONGUE

GUNNLAUG AND HRAFN: THEIR MEETING

WHAT warrior wight thus thro' the night o'er
    Norway uplands rides?
'Tis Gunnlaug strong, of serpent tongue, with kins-
    man friends and guides.
He seeks his foe, brave Hrafn the Skald, the wealthy
    Onund's son,
To end by battle's stern ordeal a strife long since
    begun.

What feud divides them? 'Tis a cause well-known,
    I wot, and old—
A woman—Helga hight "the fair"; whose locks, as
    beaten gold,

Loose-shed her limbs from head to foot with silky veil
　　could screen;
No comelier woman, so 'tis said, was ever in Iceland
　　seen,
Gunnlaug and Helga early loved. For Gunnlaug
　　long abode
With Thorstein Egilsson her sire; who to the strip-
　　ling show'd
Law-wisdom. Shrewd the teacher was; yet learn'd
　　the scholar more
From Helga's eyes and Helga's tongue of love's less
　　crabbed lore.
To earnest grew the troth first given twixt boy and
　　girl in jest:
As saith the saw, "What young we learn is still
　　remember'd best.

But Gunnlaug first abroad must fare, and, ere he
　　claim his bride,
His prowess prove. To Norway he and Ireland
　　westwards hied,
To England sail'd, saw London bridge that spans the
　　Thames' proud flood,
The Orkneys too and Sweden's realm, and won him
　　honour good.

Three kings, two earls, he knew and pleased.   The
    Swede king Olaf's hall
Held him with Hrafn, an Icelander and fellow-skald
    withal,
In friendship join'd awhile.   But both were wilful,
    and each bard
Would claim first place.   Whence soon they fell to
    bitter words and hard,
Check'd in the royal presence; yet the quarrel wax'd
    so warm
That Hrafn to Iceland sail'd resolved to work his
    rival harm.

There wooed he Helga, Gunnlaug's bride; and won
    her kinsfolk's will,
Tho' not the maid's, by slanderous tales of Gunnlaug
    absent still;
And they were wed.   Then all too late, detain'd
    perforce, return'd
Gunnlaug; and hot his wrath against the son of
    Onund burn'd.

Him at the Thing he challenged forth upon the holm
    to fight.
They fought; yet had but changed few blows, nor
    fully proved their might,

Ere kinsfolk parted them. Thus check'd, not quench'd,
    was their intent :
What friendly rede might skill to baulk such warriors'
    eager bent ?
Cold hearth and loveless home had Hrafn, a fair but
    ill-wed wife,
Her heart not his.   And while they yet should both
    abide in life,
Gunnlaug and he, no joy he hoped.   " Since kinsmen
    interfere,
And laws forbid, go we," quoth Hrafn, "where
    meddlers none are near ;
Fight we abroad."   This rede they chose ; wherefore
    by diverse ways
Eastwards they fared, and what must be now came
    despite delays.

Adown the glen rode with his men Gunnlaug that
    whole night through ;
Till at daybreak beside a lake their foemen came in
    view.
Hrafn and his band had ta'en their stand upon a
    jutting ness ;
Gunnlaug rode up. "Well met," he said.   Quoth
    Hrafn, " I say no less.

And choose thou; fight we mine and thine, or thou
    alone and I."
"Either contents me," he replied. But Grim and
    Olaf cry,
(Kinsmen of Hrafn they were) "Nay, nay, we sit not
    idle here,
While ye two fight." "Nor will I leave Gunnlaug
    my kinsman dear,"
Said Thorkell Swarthy. "Be it so," said Gunnlaug,
    "but ye guides,
Earl Eric's men, sit neutral near, and whatso hap
    betides,
Bear back the tale." Then to their work they went,
    and stoutly all
Did battle. Grim and Olaf turn on Gunnlaug both,
    yet fall,
Though twain on one: Thorkell, by Hrafn o'er-
    match'd, soon gat his bane
And, save the chiefs, at long and last fell all their
    comrades slain.

Then Hrafn and Gunnlaug whole and fierce in eager
    onset close,
With unabated force they deal and parry mighty
    blows.

Gunnlaug the gift of Ethelred, the noble English
    king,
A trenchant sword, was wielding; this on Hrafn with
    forceful swing
Down brought he, and shore off his foot: who reel'd
    yet never dropt,
But hobbling backward stay'd the stump upon a tree-
    stem propt.
Then Gunnlaug, "Thou'rt for combat now unfit; I
    will not fight
With footless man and halt."   "In truth I am in
    sorry plight,"
The other own'd, "and much have lost; yet none
    the less, I deem,
Might I bear up, could I but drink some drops from
    yonder stream."
"If water in my helm I bring," said Gunnlaug frank
    and bold,
"Deal thou not guilefully."   "No guile," said Hrafn,
    "my heart doth hold."
So Gunnlaug hasted to the brook, and stooping to
    the brink
He doff'd his helm, and drew and bare to Hrafn the
    freshening drink:

Who, while he reach'd his left hand out to take his
    foeman's gift,
On the bare head brought down his right with sudden
    swordstroke swift,
Dealing a grievous wound. "O guile unmanly,
    treacherous foe!
Cried Gunnlaug, "when I trusted thee, to strike such
    shameful blow."
"Yea, true," said Hrafn, "but sudden thought o'er-
    mastering honour came;
Helga the fair—shall he survive her dear embrace to
    claim."
With that again they furious fought; till ended thus
    the strife,
That Hrafn o'erborne by Gunnlaug fell, and yielded
    up his life.

Came then the guides, bound Gunnlaug's wound,
    who sang the while a stave,
How flash'd on Dinganess that morn the falchions of
    the brave.
The dead they buried; on his horse set Gunnlaug
    then and brought
To Lifanger. There for three days he lay, and there
    he sought

And found from holy Christian priest all ministering
    aid ;
Then died, and in the sacred mould of Church his
    limbs were laid.

HELGA'S DEATH

HELGA her husband and her love, her one first
    love, had lost:
And Iceland felt of that sad strife the deep and heavy
    cost—
Two warriors slain, two of her best. Then Thor-
    stein's dream of old
To him and many came to mind, and th' issues thence
    foretold.

For he had dream'd how on his roof a swan sat fair
    and bright,
And how two eagles bold and fierce for her waged
    jealous fight,
Till both fell dead. In grief the swan long droop'd;
    then came a third,
A falcon, and she follow'd home less sad that friendly
    bird.

"This dream of thine (his Norway guest explain'd, a
 cunning seer)
Bodes for thy daughter yet unborn two suitors void
 of fear,
Who for her love shall fight and die; a third shall be
 her mate."
These seem'd but idle words; yet deeds confirm'd
 them all too late,
When Hrafn and Gunnlaug for one love contending
 met their fate.

Long time a widow Helga sat at Borg. Her father
 then
Gave her to Thorkell Hallkellsson to wife. Mid
 doughty men
No laggard he, a wight of mark and means and skaldic
 lore:
And Helga won a restful home, and children to him
 bore.
But never more within her heart could fire of love
 burn hot,
And never through her wedded years was Gunnlaug
 bold forgot.

A cloak there was, which England's king erewhile to
    Gunnlaug gave,
Of scarlet hue and costly skins, a mantle bright and
    brave:
This at Hungerda's wedding-feast, where Gunnlaug
    met and long
With Helga talk'd, to his lost bride he left. And
    this among
Her treasures Helga prized, and oft her look thereon
    she bent,
And where her eyes were turn'd, be sure, her heart
    regretful went;
Love once by women early learnt scarce in long age
    is spent.

Now so it was that sickness sore on Thorkell's house-
    hold came,
And many suffer'd much. At last droop'd Helga
    with the same,
But took not to her bed. One eve she sat the fire
    beside
Against her husband Thorkell's knees reclined. "O
    bring," she cried,

"Gunnlaug's last gift, the cloak." 'Twas brought.
    Then sat she up, unroll'd
The robe, and for awhile she gazed on each resplendent
    fold
With wistful look: then back she sank, as weary, and
    the wife
Lapp'd in her loving husband's arms at once breathed
    out her life.

But Thorkell mourning sang: "Now lies dead in
    mine arms my fair,
My bright-robed love, my golden love.   God takes
    her to His care.
Too soon by doom untimely reft she leaves me
    lingering still,
Alone and wifeless, to endure the heavier load of ill."

FROM HALLGRIM PETURSSON

THOUGH not belonging to the early classic age of Iceland, Hallgrim Pétursson deserves no mean place among writers of sacred poetry. The spirit of hymnody that stirred Germany after the Reformation soon passed into Iceland; and of Icelandic hymn-writers Hallgrim Pétursson bears the palm. He wrote much sacred poetry, but most highly prized among his countrymen are his Passion-Psalms.

He was born about 1614, was ordained in 1644, held successively two cures in the West of Iceland, and died in 1659. He published his Passion-Psalms, fifty in number, in 1659; they had occupied him ten years. Some of the shorter pieces of Hallgrim are quite as good in their way; possibly to modern English taste they will prove more acceptable.

In the following translations the metres and rhymes of the original are kept: to reproduce exactly all the alliterations of the Icelandic I have found impossible.

PASSION-PSALMS

THESE are hymns on the events of our Lord's Passion. They have always been the delight of Icelanders : being regularly sung in the Lenten season. Each hymn might be termed a short metrical sermon on its theme. Here are two specimens.

INTRODUCTORY PSALM

1

UP, up, my soul and all my mind,
    Up, O my heart and voice combined ;
Help, thought and tongue ; for I would fain
Wake memory of our Lord's dear pain.

2

This duty biddeth holy Paul,
That we, earth's dwellers one and all,
The anguish and sad death declare
Which for our griefs our Master bare.

3

Jesus was pleased, my Saviour dear,
To die for my redemption here;
Well-pleased should I this act record
In thankfulness to Him my Lord.

4

Too late the prick of keen regret,
Too little my devotion yet!
That Jesus suffer'd in my stead,
Too seldom is rememberèd.

5

My soul, on that sweet offering
Look we, that hath with God our King
Atoned us once condemned.   Tho' sad,
A thought is here to make us glad.

6

What better calms the heart's deep woes
Than Jesu's holy pain and throes?
What best restraineth shame and sin?
His bleeding Form our mind within.

7

Where, O my soul, canst clearlier prove
The true heart-spirit of God's love—
All that thy Father's mercies mean—
Where more than here in Jesus seen?

8

Jesu, Thy spirit give to me;
So to Thy glory all shall be
Herein pourtray'd, sung, said, declared:
And be the boon by others shared!

PASSION PSALM XLIII.

"It is fulfilled."

I

THIS done, when He in order due
    Tasted the vinegar, and knew
His strength all spent, His vigour sped,
"It is fulfill'd," the Saviour said.

2

This thy Lord's word with faith and love,
My soul, 'twere well to search and prove :
If thou its true deep meaning see,
Sweet comfort will it yield to thee.

3

First must thou know that God had given
Distinct a spoken law from heaven ;
And will'd that in this world each wight,
Ruled by this law, should live aright.

4

Full righteousness, without, within,
Body, soul, mind, all pure of sin,
Offenceless words, and works the same—
The law from us made such strict claim.

5

Our thoughts, our hearts, must be aglow
With purest love; we must forego
Dissembling, anger, curse and ban,
With God and with our neighbour man.

6

Who should such righteousness attain,
He for his guerdon life should gain ;
Who should transgress but in one jot,
Eternal doom should be his lot.

7

But never man, since by his sin
Adam first fell, sufficed to win
This perfectness in all his deeds :
Such task his nature far exceeds.

8

Unbearable man's guilt became,
So stern the Master's call and claim ;
"Or let the law fulfilment find,
Or lost for ever be mankind."

9

Then Jesus our sad state espied,
Came down upon our earth to bide ;
He, offspring of high Heav'n, yet now
Humble beneath the law did bow.

10

He willing put Him in our place,
(God this accepting of His grace)
His Father He for us obey'd,
And of the law fulfilment made.

11

Further, of sins already done
That He the past guilt might atone,
And blot the law's curse from our score,
Sharp pain and shameful death He bore,

12

And having gone all duties through
That we ourselves had owed to do,
And from transgression bought us free,
This He would have us know and see.

13

Wherefore the Lord sent forth this cry
Upon the Cross, when death was nigh,
That so our peace might at the last
Stand in His merits pledged and fast.

14

Mark then, my soul, how for thy cheer
The Son of God now crieth clear:
What works thy ransom, by thy Lord
Is all fulfilled, so sounds His word.

15

Fulfill'd is now the law for thee,
Fulfill'd the price to set thee free,
Fulfill'd what prophets spake before,
Fulfill'd the grace for thee in store.

16

Jesu, I thank Thee, Sovereign Lord,
Who dost such comfort here afford:
To mend my unfulfilment frail
Oh may Thy Godhead's strength prevail!

17

Help me, that so in heart I may
On Thy example think alway,
And in the world may keep me sure,
Ruled by right faith and conscience pure.

18

On this Thy word I firm rely,
By this secured can fearless die :
Since now fulfilment by Thee wrought
My guilt hath cleansed, my freedom bought.

BURIAL HYMN

This Hymn has its proper tune (a very good one) in the Icelandic Church Hymn Book, and is often sung. Though some of the thoughts may seem trite now, they cannot have been so in Icelandic in 1660.

1

As on smooth meadow growing
  A fair and comely flower,
Its fresh pure beauty showing
  At early matin hour,
Untimely shorn soon lieth,
  With faded hues and leaf,
And in a moment dieth;—
  So man's life endeth brief.

2

Childhood goes gaily leaping,
  Old age drags heavy pace,
Death's unknown road both keeping
  Still run the self-same race.

Life gives of long fruition
  No pledge, their term none choose ;
All bear this hard condition,
  Short loan to hold and lose.

3

Death like a reaper moweth
  (True parable, I ween)
All that before him groweth
  With scythe both strong and keen.
Grass, rush, reed, green herb tender,
  The glowing flower of earth,
Even the rose's splendour,
  Alike he counts nought worth.

4

Man's life no while abideth,
  Onwards it still must wend :
Him the grave-gloom soon hideth,
  Death grips, and makes an end.
All world-ways seek one centre ;
  With light or heavy tread
We, will we nill we, enter
  One home, one-whither led.

5

Death not for state or power
  Will shrink, or one step stay:
Nor bribed by fairest dower
  One moment will delay.
He counts all one, unheeding
  Like we it well or ill;
Nor wrath nor prayerful pleading
  Can soothe his bitter will.

6

Men wade and swim in error,
  Thro' doubtful deeps they fare,
Not knowing of death's terror
  The how or when or where.
Into life's house all mortals
  One only door lets in;
By many gaping portals
  Their way thereout they win.

7

If death then hath dominion
  To hurt all worldly kind,
Dare I hold vain opinion
  That I shall pity find?

Of Adam's form and fashion
  I flesh and blood have ta'en,
And, earth by generation,
  To earth must turn again.

8

Nor right of use or seizure
  Gave me this life I hold :
The soul is borrow'd treasure
  Knit with the body's mould.
The Lord our Maker lendeth,
  And justly claims his loan ;
He death as steward sendeth
  To gather in his own.

9

Then to God's name I bow me ;
  So be it, since it must.
Less worthy I allow me
  Than many whose bones are dust.
Whene'er the Master calleth
  No man may buy him free :
And night, where'er it falleth,
  Hath nought of fear for me.

10

One Whom I love, in Heaven
   Still lives, Who doth redeem,
Jesus, my Saviour given,
   Who lives o'er all supreme.
He over death victorious
   Died once upon the Cross,
With endless life and glorious
   To countervail my loss.

11

Conquest He won, and dying
   Death's very self hath slain,
His power and might destroying;
   Nought now can work me bane.
Let earth my body cover,
   Life my free soul shall bless,
And pains be past and over
   In heavenly happiness.

12

Jesus in heart still keeping,
   Myself to Him I yield:
At home, abroad, my sleeping,
   My waking He shall shield.

My helper and defender
  Is He, my very life:
Him my heart trusts to render
  More mild death's bitter strife.

15

To Jesus I betake me,
  In Him I live, I die;
Tho' health and life forsake me,
  Yet death I can defy.
O death, I dauntless meet thee
  Powerless to work me ill;
In Christ's good strength I greet thee;
  So welcome at thy will!

MORNING HYMN

AT morn, when early I uprise,
   At eve, when rest my closing eyes,
My life and health, dear Saviour mine,
Into Thy hands I still resign.

Comfort and calm my soul hath known,
Lord Jesus, in Thy wounds alone.
Oh let Thy guiltless blood, I pray,
Hallow and bless my life alway.

Thou, bearing pain and agony,
Christ, with Thy blood my peace didst buy :
Abide with me awake, asleep,
And from all danger safely keep.

May hosts angelic shield me still!
So shall no devils work me ill.
In woe, in wealth, in grief, in glee,
Jesu my King, abide with me.

To live or die, whiche'er my lot,
My heart this issue feareth not.
O God of truth, this breath of mine
Into Thy hands I glad resign.

EVENING HYMN

O HEAVENLY Father, to my bed
    I climb, on Thee relying :
Light from Thy face upon me shed,
    Turn thou to joy my sighing.
My heart's thoughts make for Thy Name's sake
    Pure from all taint offending :
Me safely keep, sweet rest in sleep
    To soul and body sending.

Lord Jesus, Helper alway near,
    Foster my life and save me ;
As mother-nurse her infant dear,
    In Thy blood's bath oh lave me.
My soul to Thy blest wounds shall fly,
    And there be hid for ever :
And nothing may, nor now nor aye,
    Our union dissever.

Children and wife I trust to Thee,
 Spirit of God most blessèd;
Beneath Thy guard for ever be
 All goods by me possessèd.
I pray Thy might this livelong night
 Whate'er I love to tender:
May Thy pure arm stay risk and harm,
 My helper and defender!

And last, when sleep doth on me fall,
 Sweet gracious Trinity,
Purge me from guilt, and so I shall
 Unfearing live to Thee.
Bid by me stand Thine angel band,
 So me no sin shall stain;
But Thee always my heart shall praise
 For all Thy help.   Amen.

MORNING AND EVENING
VERSES

THESE were meant for use at family prayers. There are many
pairs of them. Two examples are given. The metres are those
of the original.

MORNING

GOD grant us one and all good day,
    Good day our home, ourselves to brighten:
God speed His children's work and way,
    God all our labours lighten.
Jesu, God's Son, grant us Thy peace,
Gladness in every kind outpour.
Help, Holy Ghost; with healthful grace
Hover our busy household o'er,
    This day and evermore.

EVENING

GOD grant us one and all good night,
  Good night our home, ourselves, o'ershading;
God grant us slumber's sweet respite,
  Our lighten'd labours aiding.
Jesu, God's Son, grant us Thy peace,
Guarding our every work and store.
Help, Holy Ghost, with healthful grace
Hover our resting household o'er
  This night and evermore.

MORNING

RISEN is the Sun, and clear
  Shines in the East his ray:
His heat our earthly sphere
Feels, and again laughs gay:
And praises Thee our King
Eager with full acclaim,
Who hear'st weak warblers sing
Glory to God's great name.

EVENING

SWIFT sinks the Sun below
    Yon hills that bound our sight,
Nearer and gloomier grow
The shades and ills of night.
Dark is our dwelling here,
Dangers beset our way:
O living Jesu, cheer
My path with lightening ray.

GOSPEL VERSES

OF these sonnets (as they might almost be called) on the Gospels there is a complete set for all the Sundays and some Chief Holy Days of the Christian year. It is noticeable that the Gospel passages correspond to our Prayer-Book Gospels. Each verse is on the same model: a quatrain of fact: a quatrain of lesson: a triplet of prayer or praise.

CHRISTMAS NIGHT

St. Luke ii. 1-14

JESUS was born on Christmas night,
  And laid in manger bare:
Hell's devils trembled with affright,
  Heaven's angels sang in air.
May He our help, O God of Love,
  That flesh-veil'd Saviour be!
His Manhood pure our healing prove
  Now and eternally!
Heaven let God's glory fill,
Let peace earth's tumults still,
God's people find good-will!

4TH SUNDAY AFTER EPIPHANY

St. Matthew viii., 23-27

GOD'S Son on the ship was riding,
  The restless sea 'gan chafe:
He, storm to stillness chiding,
  Straight made the voyage safe.
To Thee my cry, Lord, tendeth,
  For many my perils be;
Grant me, when life's storm endeth,
  Land, haven, rest with Thee.
May all things, Saviour mine,
  Revere Thy power divine;
  Honour and praise be Thine!

3RD SUNDAY AFTER TRINITY

St. Luke xv.

SON, silver, sheep, when they
  All lost and wandering were,
Father, wife, herd, straightway
  To seek and find did fare.

In mercy so God's Son
  Bears rich and ready aid ;
By each repentant one
  God's angels glad are made.
 A son, a silver coin
 Of price, a sheep of Thine,
 Make me, my Lord Divine.

NOTES

NOTES TO PROSE

THOR AND HRUNGNIR

Page 1. *Sleipnir.*—" Swift-slipper," the legendary horse of eight legs, which Magnússon thinks represents the wind, the points of the compass being eight in old time.

Page 2. *Grjotuna-gard.*—" Stone-fence."

Page 4. *Mökkur-calf.*—*Mökkur* means " dense cloud " : the proverbial stupidity of giants may be hinted at, *vis consili expers.*

Page 6. *Örvandil.*—By some identified with Orion.

SIF'S HAIR

Page 7. *Skidbladnir.*—" A boat sheathed or covered with many patches " (Magnússon). But he suggests now that the first syllable may have been originally *skinn*, which would describe some boat of a coracle kind, portable.

Page 9. *Air and water.*—Like those of Hermes " that bare him swift as the wind over land and sea."

OTTER'S FINE

Page 15. *Lay on the gold.*—Serpents brood over and guard gold in these legends.

Page 18. *Valkyria.*—These "choosers of the slain" were battle goddesses or divine beings. Brynhildr, however, seems to have been a mortal, being king Atli's brother.

Page 21. *Snake-pit.*—This kind of punishment appears several times in northern stories. Ragnar Lodbrok was so put to death.

Page 23. *Featherless.*—Egil, on the loss of his son Bodvar, sings : "Weak-winged I fly, when friends all fail."

FRODI'S MILL

Page 26. *Grotti.*—The word is akin to "grit," "groats." The sea is called *skerja-grotti*, "skerry-grinder," "rock-grinder."

Ibid. No longer.—It seems to be a sort of proverb for wakefulness. The poem Grotti-song has "Sleep no longer than does the cock."

HEDIN'S HOST

Page 28. *Dains-leif.*—Dain was the name of a dwarf. Dwarves were workers in iron, according to the old stories.

Ibid. To vaunt.—Not unlike Ahab's answer to Benhadad, "Let not him that girdeth on his harness boast himself as he that putteth it off."

Page 29. *Renewed.*—The dying and renewing of the host may be (and, I fancy, by some is) explained as a parable of natural phenomena. Sometimes groups of stones may by their shapes have suggested slain warriors turned to stone.

THE BATTLE OF VINHEATH

Page 32. *Enhazel.*—The process is explained further on : the lexicon refers to two other passages that mention this curious kind of challenge to a pitched battle.

Page 36. *Earls-ness.*—Said by Petersen to be in Wales.   Any way, it must have been on the west coast.

Page 39. *Loose in array.*—This would describe Scotch High-landers' tactics for later times.

Page 44. *A ring.*—Such arm-rings were much worn by kings and great ones, and presents given from them.

Page 45. *Two chests.*—These Egil inherited from Skallagrim, and buried just before his death ; nor were they ever found.

GUNNLAUG'S STORY

Page 54. *Biting in words.*—His name here explained as fitting his nature : it was, however, inherited from his grandfather.

Page 58. *Nidaros.*—The town at the mouth of the Nid, afterwards Trondhjem.

Page 60. *The same death.*—By violence.

Page 63. *Blunts, i.e.,* by spells.   But Thororm put the spell on the wrong weapon.

Page 71. *Our friendship end.*—After this Hrafn supplants Gunnlaug with Helga's father ; and the feud is carried out to its fatal end.   The chief scenes of the rest of the Saga are given later on as ballads.

FROM THE WATERDALESMEN'S STORY

Page 73. *Jamtaland.*—In the north of Sweden.   From Raums-dale it lies about west.

Page 74. *Coddle.*—This rebuke by Ketill of home-hugging and baking by the fire recalls Pindar's words : " Why should one coddle idly a nameless old age sitting in the dark, a stranger to all noble deeds ?"—*Ol.,* i. 133.

 NOTES TO PROSE

THORODD SNORRI'S SON

Page 92. *Talking-matches.*—Much like what comes later between the kings Sigurd and Eystein. From a note of Kirkpatrick on Ps. cxxvii. 5, it appears that the Arabs have such "boasting-matches," which sometimes led to fierce feuds.

FROM SIGURD'S SAGA

Page 102. *Gilli Christ.*—"Servant of Christ." He did not afterwards act up to his name; but broke promises and became a cruel king.

Page 108. *Such attacks.*—By these Sigurd's character was much impaired towards the end of his reign, which outlasted Eystein's.

Page 113. *Comparisons.*—A full description of a kind of boasting-match that is mentioned elsewhere.

Page 118. *A knot.*—What conditions Sigurd here set for his brother does not appear; but Eystein's reply seems to say he could have put his brother in a fix on his return.

Page 119. *Gold-necks.*—For all your showy deeds, mine have been more useful. We do not wonder that the two were not very good friends after this. It appears from history that the early part of the reign of these two kings was peaceable and orderly; that much was really done (especially by Eystein) in the way of improvements. And Sigurd's participation in the Crusades brought his people into communication with the civilisation of the south of Europe. (*Cf.* Willson's *Hist. of the Church in Norway*, ch. ix., pp. 111-114.)

NOTES TO VERSE

WAYFARERS' LAY

Page 124, stanza 2. *Hell.*—The place here : sometimes the word is used for the goddess. I cannot see that here *Niflhel* differs from *Hel.* Odin rides to *Niflhel* and meets the hound coming thence. *Nifl* means "mist"; *cf.* Greek νεφέλη.

Page 126, stanza 6. *Wayfarer.*—Some render "waywise," "warwise."

Ibid., stanza 7. *Gleeful.*—The original is rather obscure; but probably it describes the glad anticipation of Balder's company at Hell's high table. Gray, following Bartholin, supposes the *as-megir* are the gods still in Asgard, and the feeling (*of væni*) to be "grief."

Page 127, stanza 9. *Renowned.*—Though used for an evil deed the mistletoe would become famed in story.

Page 128, stanza 11. *Wield.*—An infant Hercules, *in cunis jam Jove dignus.* It is not made certain when the slaying of Hoder was to be ; it might be some time after the one-night-old child bore weapons. Some interval is surely implied by "he shall not wash . . . till." Harold Lufa's vow at once occurs to us.

Page 128, stanza 12. *Maidens.*—Mason on Gray thinks these were "the Nornir, invisible to mortals; and therefore Odin thus betrays himself to be a god."

Page 129, stanza 14. *Doom.*—This used to be rendered "twilight." And certain poems have familiarised us with this. But, however gloom and evening may suit the world's end, it is now agreed that in *ragna-rök* the last syllable is not *rökr*, "twilight," but *rök*, "judgment."

THE MILL-SONG

Page 132, stanza 6. *House-crower.*—"Hall-cuckoo" literally. It seems likely that the name of the cuckoo is imitative, from its note. So, too, are some names of the cock, which is meant here.

Page 134, stanzas 10-13. *Playmates.*—First these maidens worked underground, then in battles, then were put thus to slaves' work; which ends in death for their hard master.

Page 138, stanza 21. *Son of Yrsa.*—The exact meaning of this genealogy I do not presume to fathom.

HEAD-RANSOM

Page 140, stanza 1. *Mind a galleon.*—Dante more than once speaks of his poetry or himself as a ship: *e.g.*, "Per correr miglior acqua alza le vele omai la navicella del mio ingegno."—*Purg.* I. 1.

Page 144, stanza 12. *Ogress' beast.*—The wolf.

SONS' LOSS

Page 153, stanza 13. *Brotherless.*—Thorolf, his elder brother, fell at Vinheath.

Page 154, stanza 15. *None in brother's stead.*—Thus too argues Antigone in Sophocles (l. 912) that brother is more irreplaceable than child or husband.

Page 155, stanza 17. *Bees' home.*—He means some heavenly abode of bliss. The word is *bý-skip*, "bee-skip." Though Icelanders had no bees, Egil might know well about them, might even in England have heard the word "bee-skep" (or skip) often. In the Viking Club's *Saga Book*, 1901, is a paper on this passage.

ARINBJORN'S EPIC

Page 160, stanza 3. *Yngling's son.*—All kings were supposed to be descended from him. Eric Bloodaxe is meant.

Page 161, stanza 6. *Bolstermate's ransom, i.e,* Head-ransom. Some curious kennings follow. "Ear-mouth drank" reminds the classical scholar of Horace's *bibit aure vulgus.* "Hood-knoll" means "head."

Page 162, stanza 9. *Tooth-fence.*—Homer's frequent ἕρκος ὀδόντων.

Page 164, stanza 12. *Fair-haired.*—Harold Fairhair slew Thorolf the elder, Skallagrim's brother.

Ibid., stanza 13. *Of the sea-mew.*—"The sea" : so also what ollows. Sea-steeds are "ships."

Page 165, stanza 16. *Voice-plane.*—"The tongue," as shaping the articulate sounds.

Page 166, stanza 17. *Hearth-fire.*—*Arin* means "hearth" ; *bjorn*, "bear."

Ibid., stanza 18. *Njord.*—God of wealth and traffic.

Page 167, stanza 21. *Shafted.*—Not many can help generously all. Repairs of weapons might be a frequent need in that age.

Page 168, stanza 23. *Of Draupnir.*—The legend of the ring is told in " Sif's Hair."

Page 169, stanza 25. *Battles.*—If there was ever any more of this poem, some of it may have come here.

BALLADS FROM NJALSSAGA

Gunnar, The Burning.—For permission to reprint these two I am indebted to the kindness of Messrs. Blackwood.

Page 188. *Twelve ells.*—Something more than twenty-four feet.

FROM GUNNLAUG'S SAGA

Page 221, line 1. *Helga.*—She had married Thorkell : he was the falcon of the dream.

HALLGRIM PÉTURSSON

Page 237, stanza 6. *Swim.*—The later and usual sense of *svima* is "to be dizzy." But possibly Hallgrim used it in the older sense. He seems to mean something like Wolsey's :

> " I have ventured
> Like little wanton boys that swim on bladders,
> This many summers in a sea of glory,
> But far beyond my depth."
>
> *Henry VIII.*, Act III., Scene 2.

Page 238, stanza 9. *Night.*—It is a sort of proverb of one who lets his lodging be where night may overtake him on his way ; of one who is not over anxious to provide against the future.